REVISE EDEXCEL GCSE

Science

Additional Science

REVISION WORKBOOK

Higher

Series Consultant: Harry Smith

Series Editor: Penny Johnson

Authors: Peter Ellis, Damian Riddle, Ian Roberts, Julia Salter

- -

A note from the publisher

In order to ensure that this resource offers high-quality support for the associated Edexcel qualification, it has been through a review process by the awarding body to confirm that it fully covers the teaching and learning content of the specification or part of a specification at which it is aimed, and demonstrates an appropriate balance between the development of subject skills, knowledge and understanding, in addition to preparation for assessment.

While the publishers have made every attempt to ensure that advice on the qualification and its assessment is accurate, the official specification and associated assessment guidance materials are the only authoritative source of information and should always be referred to for definitive guidance.

Edexcel examiners have not contributed to any sections in this resource relevant to examination papers for which they have responsibility.

No material from an endorsed resource will be used verbatim in any assessment set by Edexcel.

Endorsement of a resource does not mean that the resource is required to achieve this Edexcel qualification, nor does it mean that it is the only suitable material available to support the qualification, and any resource lists produced by the awarding body shall include this and other appropriate resources.

For the full range of Pearson revision titles across GCSE, BTEC and AS Level visit:
www.pearsonschools.co.uk/revise

ALWAYS LEARNING

PEARSON

Contents

A small bit of small print

Edexcel publishes Sample Assessment Material and the Specification on its website. This is the official content and this book should be used in conjunction with it. The questions in this book have been written to help you practise what you have learned in your revision. Remember: the real exam questions may not look like this.

Target grade ranges

Target grade ranges are quoted in this book for some of the questions. Students targeting this grade range should be aiming to get most of the marks available. Students targeting a higher grade should be aiming to get all of the marks available.

Plant and animal cells

D-B 1 The diagram shows a type of cell.

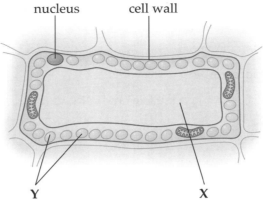

a) Which types of organism have cells like this?

....

(1 mark)

b) Give the names of the organelles labelled **X** and **Y**.

X: ....   Y: ....

(2 marks)

c) State **two** roles of the nucleus.

....

....

(2 marks)

D-B 2 The table shows some organelles that are present in cells. Some cells do not contain all these
organelles. Complete the table to show which organelles are present in plants and animals.

> Guided

For each organelle, you should also describe its role in the cell.

> On every page you will find a guided question. Guided questions have
> part of the answer filled in for you to show you how best to answer them.

Organelle	Plant	Animal	Role
chloroplast	✓	✗	site of photosynthesis
cytoplasm			
mitochondria			
vacuole			

(8 marks)

C-A 3 Compare the roles of the cell membrane and the cell wall.

> Your answer should mention the main roles of the two structures.

....

....

....

(2 marks)

Inside bacteria

D-B

> **Guided**

1 Scientists use two types of microscopes to examine cells: light microscopes and electron microscopes. Complete the passage below, which describes how these types of microscope are different.

Light microscopes magnify ....

than electron microscopes.

The level of detail seen in a light microscope is .... than the level seen

with ....

(4 marks)

D-B

2 The picture shows a typical bacterium.

a) Which feature of animal cells is not present in bacteria?

....

....

(1 mark)

membrane

cell wall

b) Bacteria have two types of DNA present in their cells.

i) What are these two types of DNA called?

....

....

(2 marks)

ii) Which of these two types of DNA carries most genetic information?

....

(1 mark)

B-A*

3 A doctor wants to examine some bacteria. He can use a light microscope, which magnifies by 2000 ×, or an electron microscope, which magnifies by 100 000 ×.

a) How much more magnification will the doctor get with the electron microscope?

....

....

(2 marks)

EXAM ALERT

b) The bacteria he wants to look at are 2 μm long.

i) Calculate the size of the magnified image of the bacteria formed by each microscope.

> Students have struggled with exam questions similar to this in the past – **be prepared!** ResultsPlus

> Students often make mistakes in exam questions when they have to convert a number in non-standard units.
> Remember that 1 μm = 1 × 10^{-6} m

(3 marks)

ii) Use your answer to explain which is the best microscope to use.

....

....

(2 marks)

DNA

D-B

> **Guided**

1 Our chromosomes contain genetic information. This information is held in our DNA.

Describe the difference between **chromosomes**, **genes** and **DNA**.

> This question is best answered by thinking of the definition of each of these terms.

Chromosomes are a collection of genes ....

....

....

(3 marks)

D-B

2 This is a diagram showing a short section of a DNA molecule.

a) What name is given to the shape of a DNA molecule?

....

(1 mark)

b) The DNA molecule is made up of a series of bases.

i) Name the bases present in DNA.

....

....

(2 marks)

ii) Describe how the two strands of the DNA molecule are joined together.

....

....

(2 marks)

B-A*

3 Explain how the following substances are useful when extracting DNA from cells.

a) Detergent

....

....

....

(2 marks)

b) Ethanol

....

....

....

(2 marks)

DNA discovery

D-B   **1**   Two teams of scientists were involved in working out the structure of DNA.

Guided

Describe how each team of scientists contributed to working out the structure of the DNA molecule.

Wilkins and Franklin, were looking at ....

....This was important because ....

....

Watson and Crick, were looking at ....

....This was important because it allowed them to

....

(4 marks)

C-A   **2**   The Human Genome Project has mapped all the genetic information in human DNA.

   a)   Explain the difference between genes and the genome.

   ....

   ....

   (2 marks)

   b)   Explain why the project involved many scientists working together.

   ....

   ....

   (2 marks)

B-A*   **3**   The Human Genome Project has given scientists access to a great deal of information about our genes. Discuss the advantages and disadvantages of this.

> If you are asked for advantages and disadvantages try to give at last one example of each.

....

....

....

....

(4 marks)

Genetic engineering

D-B   **1**   People with diabetes rely on the substance insulin. Human insulin can be produced by genetically modified bacteria, produced through genetic engineering. Explain the role of **a)** a human gene, **b)** enzymes and **c)** bacteria in the production of insulin.

Guided

    a)   The human gene needed is ....

        It is needed because ....

                                                                        (2 marks)

    b)   ....

        ....

                                                                        (2 marks)

    c)   ....

        ....

                                                                        (2 marks)

D-B   **2**   Crops, such as tomatoes, are often genetically modified.

    a)   Name one plant that has been genetically modified to improve its nutritional value.

        ....

                                                                        (1 mark)

    b)   Explain how this modification is of benefit to humans.

        ....

        ....

        ....

        ....

        ....

> The increased nutritional value mentioned in question **b** is a benefit to humans, but as the question tells you this, what you need to do is to explain what the modification is and why it is beneficial.

                                                                        (2 marks)

    c)   Some people have concerns about transferring new genes into plants, such as in the production of GM tomatoes, or in making plants herbicide-resistant. Describe why these concerns arise.

        ....

        ....

                                                                        (2 marks)

B-A*   **3**   Human insulin can be produced by genetically modified bacteria. Discuss the advantages and disadvantages of this process.

        ....

        ....

        ....

        ....

                                                                        (4 marks)

Mitosis

D-B **1** Cells in the body are produced through a process of cell division.

    a) Name the cell division process used to make human body cells.

    .... **(1 mark)**

    b) State the number of daughter cells produced by each cell that undergoes this process. Place a cross in the box (☒) next to your answer.

      ☐ **A** 1   ☐ **B** 2   ☐ **C** 3   ☐ **D** 4

                                                            (1 mark)

    c) Which of the following statements about the daughter cells is correct? Place a cross in the box (☒) next to your answer.

      ☐ **A** Haploid and genetically identical to parent cells.

      ☐ **B** Haploid and genetically different to parent cells.

      ☐ **C** Diploid and genetically identical to parent cells.

      ☐ **D** Diploid and genetically different to parent cells.   **(1 mark)**

D-B **2** A cell divides by mitosis every hour. How many cells will there be after four hours?

Guided

    To start there is 1 cell. After 1 hour, this divides into 2 cells.

    After 2 hours, these divide to form .... cells.

    After 3 hours, these divide to form .... cells.

    After 4 hours, these divide to form .... cells.   **(1 mark)**

D-B **3** Two types of cell division take place in the human body: one type for sex cells and the other type for other body cells.

    a) State where the chromosomes are found in the cell.

    .... **(1 mark)**

    b) Describe why human body cells are described as diploid.

    ....

    .... **(2 marks)**

    c) Body cells contain 46 chromosomes. Sex cells are haploid. State the number of chromosomes in a sex cell.

    .... **(1 mark)**

B-A* **4** Plants can reproduce asexually using mitosis. Describe how this process produces offspring plants.

> Your answer should give a description of mitosis; but also needs to relate to the question on plants reproducing asexually. You should, therefore, give some examples of how this process works in plants.

    ....

    ....

    ....

    ....

    .... **(4 marks)**

Fertilisation and meiosis

D-B

1 The following passage describes an important process in reproduction.

> Human gametes are **haploid** cells. During sexual reproduction, these **gametes** come together. This produces a zygote.

Guided

a) Describe what is meant by the terms in bold in the passage.

Haploid means half the number of chromosomes.

Gametes are ....

(2 marks)

b) Name both types of cell that are human gametes.

....

....

(2 marks)

c) Describe what happens in the process of fertilisation.

....

(1 mark)

B-A*

2 A cell contains 20 chromosomes. It undergoes division by meiosis.

a) How many chromosomes are there:

i) after the replication of DNA in the first step of meiosis?

....

(1 mark)

ii) in the daughter cells?

....

(1 mark)

b) Explain why the daughter cells are not genetically identical.

....

....

(2 marks)

B-A*

EXAM ALERT

3 Explain how mitosis and meiosis are different from each other.

....

....

....

....

....

....

(4 marks)

Students have struggled with exam questions similar to this in the past – **be prepared!** ResultsPlus

It is easy to confuse the two processes mitosis and meiosis. Make sure you learn how many daughter cells are made by each process, and how many chromosomes are produced. You should be able to explain how the divisions give these results.

Clones

D-B

Guided

1 'Snuppy' is a dog that was cloned from another dog by scientists at a university in South Korea.

Place the steps in the process of producing Snuppy in the correct order.

☐ electrical stimulus applied

☐ body cell removed from adult dog

☐ nucleus from body cell placed into enucleated egg cell

☐ embryo grows

☐ nucleus removed from egg cell

(3 marks)

B-A*

2 In March 2012, scientists in India announced that they had produced a cloned goat called Noori. Two cells were needed to produce Noori. One of these cells was a body cell from an adult female goat and the other was an enucleated egg cell from another goat. Noori is from a rare species of goat with very high-quality wool.

a) What is meant by the term 'enucleated'?

....

(1 mark)

b) Describe how the body cell from the female goat is used in the process of cloning.

....

....

....

(3 marks)

c) The goat that gave birth to Noori was unrelated to Noori. What name is given to the organism from which a clone is born?

....

(1 mark)

d) Explain what gender Noori is.

> It is important to read the question carefully. If you're not sure of the answer here, then re-read the question – and remember that a clone is genetically identical to its parent.

....

....

(2 marks)

e) Other than for scientific interest, explain one reason why people are interested in producing cloned animals such as Noori.

....

....

(2 marks)

Stem cells

D-B 1 In a recent survey, 1250 people in the UK were asked if they supported embryonic stem cell research. A total of 775 people supported the research.

a) What percentage of people supported embryonic stem cell research?

Answer .... %

(2 marks)

b) State two reasons why people might not support embryonic stem cell research.

> This question is slightly unusual. Most of the time, questions on ethical issues such as this will ask you to give an opinion. With such questions, remember to give arguments *for* and *against* before making a conclusion. Here, you can just list reasons why some people are against embryo research.

....

....

(2 marks)

D-B 2 Stem cells are found in both adults and embryos.

> ⟩ **Guided**
>
> **EXAM ALERT**

> Students have struggled with exam questions similar to this in the past – **be prepared!**   ResultsPlus

> When you are asked to describe differences, remember that for each difference you have to say something about both the things you are comparing.

Describe two ways in which these stem cells are different from each other.

All the cells in an embryo are ...., but in an adult, stem cells are

found only ....

Embryonic stem cells can differentiate into ....,

but adult stem cells can only differentiate into ....   **(4 marks)**

B-A* 3 Adult stem cells can be extracted from bone marrow of a donor. These stem cells may be implanted into a patient with leukaemia, where they differentiate to produce white blood cells.

a) Describe what is meant by the term 'differentiate'.

....

....

(2 marks)

b) Suggest why this treatment is not always successful in treating the person with leukaemia.

....

....

(2 marks)

c) Explain why embryonic stem cells have more potential than adult stem cells for helping treat people with other conditions.

....

....

(2 marks)

11

Protein synthesis

D-B   **1**   Our DNA holds the genetic code for making all the proteins in the human body.

   a)   Two of the bases in DNA are cytosine and guanine. Name the other two.

   ....

   ....

   (2 marks)

   b)   Name the small units that make up proteins.

   ....

   (1 mark)

D-B   **2**   The first step of protein synthesis involves producing a strand of RNA in the nucleus.

   a)   Give the name of this type of RNA.

   ....

   (1 mark)

   b)   What name is given to the process in which it is made?

   ....

   (1 mark)

⟩ **Guided** ⟩   **c)**   Describe two ways in which this type of RNA is different from the original DNA.

   This type of RNA has .... strand, whereas DNA has two.

   DNA contains the base thymine, whereas this type of RNA contains ....

   (2 marks)

   d)   The RNA strand made contains a different sequence of bases to the original DNA. Put a cross in the box (☒) next to the term used to describe the relationship between the RNA and DNA strands.

   ☐ **A** complementary   ☐ **B** hydrogen bonded

   ☐ **C** opposite   ☐ **D** translated

   (1 mark)

B-A*   **3**   Proteins are made at the ribosomes in cells. The ribosomes 'read' a strand of RNA.

   a)   The RNA molecule is said to have a series of codons. What is a codon?

   ....

   (1 mark)

   b)   Explain the role of transfer RNA in the process of protein manufacture.

   ....

   ....

   ....

   (3 marks)

   c)   Give the name of this part of the process of protein manufacture.

   ....

   (1 mark)

Proteins and mutations

D–B   **1**   State the three possible effects of a mutation.

> **Guided**

A mutation can be beneficial, ... or ....
          (1 mark)

D–B   **2**   Some cells were grown in a laboratory. The cells were exposed to different doses of radiation and checked to see how many mutations occurred. The results are shown in the table below.

Relative radiation dose	Number of mutations
0.2	6
0.4	11
0.6	18
0.8	25
1.0	31

a) Plot a graph of these results, and draw a line of best fit through the points.

        (3 marks)

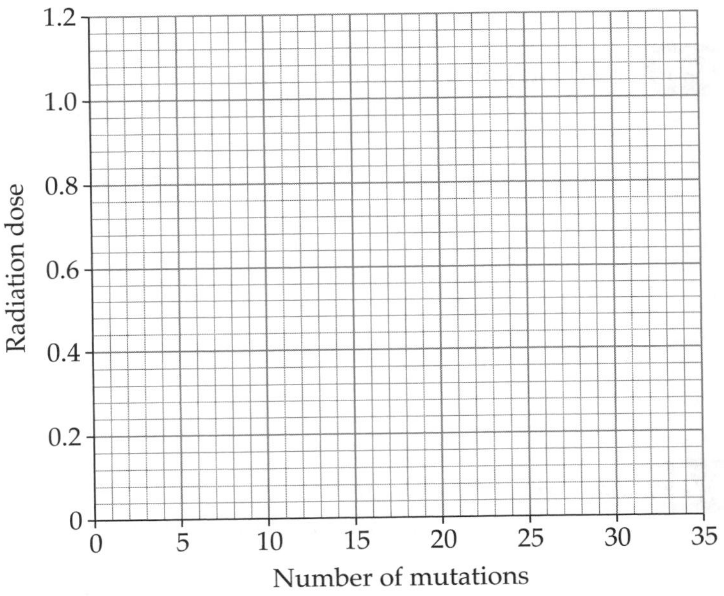

b) Describe what the graph shows about the relationship between the radiation dose and the number of mutations in the cells.

....

....

....

....

....

....

        (2 marks)

Graph: y-axis "Radiation dose" from 0 to 1.2; x-axis "Number of mutations" from 0 to 35.

B–A*   **3**   Red blood cells contain the protein haemoglobin. A mutation in the haemoglobin can change its structure, leading to sickle-shaped blood cells. These are crescent shapes, not discs. In African countries, there is some link between sickle-cells and resistance to malaria.

Suggest how this mutation can be both beneficial and harmful.

> You should think about the effect of the shape of sickle cells on the way in which the blood cells function, but also look at information in the question about possible benefits.

....

....

....

        (3 marks)

Enzymes

D-B   **1**   Many enzymes are involved in digestion in the body.

⟩Guided⟩   **a)**   Complete the table to show where the enzymes in the table have their action, and the substrate for the enzyme.

Enzyme	Where it acts	Substrate
amylase	Mouth	
lipase		

(4 marks)

b)   Explain why it is important that we have enzymes to digest our food.

....

....

....

(3 marks)

D-B   **2**   Maggie is writing a project on enzymes. She writes, 'Enzymes are living organisms. They speed up reactions in the body. Enzymes are biological molecules called lipids'.

State **two** mistakes that Maggie has made in the passage.

....

....

> To answer this question, you should both identify and correct the mistakes in the passage.

....

....

(2 marks)

B-A*   **3**   Many brands of washing powders are called 'biological' because they contain enzymes. These enzymes help to break down food stains on clothes.

a)   A T-shirt has an egg stain on it. Eggs are rich in protein. Explain what type of enzyme may be needed to break down egg stains on clothes.

....

....

....

(2 marks)

b)   Explain why biological washing powders work better below 40°C.

....

....

....

....

(3 marks)

Enzyme action

D-B 1 A student investigated the activity of lipase in different conditions.

  a) Name a suitable substrate for the enzyme lipase.

  ....

  (1 mark)

Guided b) His experiment used an initial substrate concentration of 1 unit, at 20°C. Complete
    the table to show whether the new condition would increase or decrease the rate of
    reaction, or have no effect.

New condition	Substrate concentration of 2 units	Increase to 30°C	Bubble oxygen into substrate
Effect on rate	increase		

  (3 marks)

D-B 2 The enzyme amylase breaks down starch in the small intestine. The pH in the small
    intestine is about pH 8. Explain why the reaction would be different if the conditions in the
    small intestine were acidic.

  > In this question, think about what happens to the rate if the pH were made acidic, then think about
  > why this effect would be noticed. Words that might help you include: specific, active site, denatured.

  ....

  ....

  ....

  (3 marks)

B-A* 3 The graph shows the activity of an enzyme that is
    found in bacteria in hot water springs in Iceland.

  a) State the optimum temperature for
    this enzyme.

    ....

    ....

    (1 mark)

  b) Explain why the activity of this enzyme is greater at 60°C than at 30°C.

  ....

  ....

  (2 marks)

  c) Use your knowledge of the structure and function of enzymes to explain the shape of
    the graph above 70°C.

  ....

  ....

  ....

  (3 marks)

15

Had a go ☐ Nearly there ☐ Nailed it! ☐

Biology extended writing 1

In order to grow and to reproduce, organisms use two processes for cell division. These processes are mitosis and meiosis.

Compare when these two processes occur, how they occur and the cells they produce.

(6 marks)

You will be more successful in extended writing questions if you plan your answer before you start writing. The question asks you to compare the two ways in which cells divide. You need to point out similarities and differences between the processes that you are comparing.

The features of the processes that you should consider when answering this question are:

- where each type of cell division takes place
- the numbers of daughter cells produced
- how the daughter cells compare to the parent cell
- the number of chromosomes in the daughter cells
- the types of cell that use this type of cell division.

Remember that a good answer will include good scientific terminology. In this case, terms for you to use in your answer may include: haploid, diploid, chromosome, gametes, mitosis, meiosis.

....

....

....

....

....

....

....

....

....

....

....

....

....

....

....

....

....

....

....

Biology extended writing 2

Human insulin is a protein that contains 51 amino acids in sequence. Describe how the insulin protein is made from the DNA in our cells.

(6 marks)

> You will be more successful in extended writing questions if you plan your answer before you start writing. This question covers the series of processes involved in protein manufacture, from the original DNA to the final protein.
>
> You should already know that the two processes involved are transcription and translation – so all you have to do is fill in the details for each process.
>
> It is easy to get the processes involved here confused, so be very careful when deciding how to structure your answer. Your answer could explain the following points:
>
> * which part of the DNA contains the information to make insulin
> * how the information from the DNA is transferred around the cell
> * where in the cell the manufacture of insulin takes place
> * how the information is used to decide which amino acids make up the final protein
> * how each amino acid is added to the chain making protein.

....

....

....

....

....

....

....

....

....

....

....

....

....

....

....

....

....

....

....

Aerobic respiration

D-B 1 Read the following passage and answer the questions that follow.

Aerobic respiration happens in muscle cells in the body. The muscle cells are surrounded by blood vessels. The materials needed for respiration are transferred to the muscle cells by diffusion, and the waste products are removed.

a) Name the materials needed for respiration in muscle cells.

....

(1 mark)

Guided **b)** State the meaning of the term diffusion.

Diffusion is the movement of substances from .... to .... concentration.

(1 mark)

D-B 2 Describe how respiration is different from breathing.

EXAM ALERT

....

....

....

....

> Students often confuse these two terms. ResultsPlus
>
> Make sure you know where respiration takes place and where breathing takes place, and use this in your answers.

(2 marks)

B-A* 3 The blood supplies cells with the substances needed for aerobic respiration, as well as removing waste products.

a) Write a word equation for aerobic respiration.

....

(2 marks)

b) State the name of the blood vessels that carry blood to the respiring cells.

....

(1 mark)

c) Describe the process in which substances are exchanged between blood and respiring cells. Your answer should state the direction in which each gas moves during the exchange.

....

....

....

....

(4 marks)

d) Explain why it is important for blood to be flowing past the cells in order for this process to happen efficiently.

....

....

(2 marks)

Exercise

D-B 1 Cardiac output can be calculated using the equation:
cardiac output = heart rate × stroke volume.

   a) What is meant by the term **stroke volume**?

   .... **(1 mark)**

   b) A man has a heart rate of 60 beats/minute and an average stroke volume of 75 cm³.

   i) Calculate his cardiac output.

   Cardiac output .... cm³/minute
                                        (2 marks)

   ii) Explain the change in cardiac output when the man starts to exercise.

   ....

   ....

   ....
                                        (3 marks)

B-A* 2 The graph shows the pulse rate of an athlete at rest, and after 5 minutes of different types of exercise.

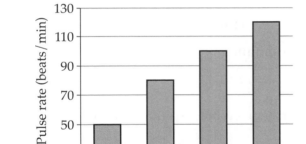

Students often struggle with calculations where they are asked to rearrange a formula. **Results**Plus

Remember to show all your steps in the calculation.

   a) Calculate the percentage increase in pulse rate between jogging and running.

   100 beats/min − 80 beats/min = 20 beats/min

   (20/80) x 100 =

                              Percentage increase ....
                                        (3 marks)

   b) Suggest why the pulse rate is highest when the athlete is rowing.

   ....

   ....
                                        (2 marks)

   c) The pulse is a measure of heart rate. At rest, the cardiac output of the athlete is 4000 cm³/min. Calculate the stroke volume, in cm³, of the athlete at rest.

                              Stroke volume .... cm³
                                        (3 marks)

Anaerobic respiration

D-B 1 A student is late for school and has to run to catch his bus. When he sits down on the bus, he feels a pain in his side. It also takes a few minutes for his breathing to return to normal.

a) Give the name of the substance responsible for the pain in his side.

.... **(1 mark)**

b) How does his breathing rate change as he runs for the bus?

....
.... **(1 mark)**

Guided c) Explain why he needed to use anaerobic respiration to catch the bus.

He had to run fast, so his muscles ....

He cannot use aerobic respiration alone because ....

.... **(2 marks)**

D-B 2 Humans can respire in two ways: using oxygen (aerobic) and without using oxygen (anaerobic).

EXAM ALERT

a) Describe how the energy output of these two methods is different.

....
....

| Students often give simple answers here, such as 'There is not enough oxygen'.   ResultsPlus |
| Make sure that you understand what is produced in both aerobic and anaerobic respiration. |

(1 mark)

b) Write a word equation for anaerobic respiration.

....
.... **(2 marks)**

c) Describe the circumstances under which anaerobic respiration occurs.

....
....
.... **(2 marks)**

B-A* 3 The graph shows how oxygen consumption changes before, during and after exercise. Explain the shape of this graph.

| You need to explain the different parts of this curve in terms of the amount of oxygen being used in respiration. Do not forget to describe the shaded area marked 'EPOC'. |

....
....
....
.... **(4 marks)**

Photosynthesis

D-B 1 Plant leaves are specially adapted for photosynthesis to take place.

a) Name the structure labelled X. Put a cross in the box (☒) next to your answer.

☐ **A** vacuole   ☐ **B** chloroplast

☐ **C** stoma   ☐ **D** palisade cell

(1 mark)

Guided b) Describe the role of the structure labelled Y.

Y is a .... Its role is to ....

....

(2 marks)

c) Describe why it is important for leaves to have a large surface area.

The large surface area means that they collect more ....

needed for ....   **(2 marks)**

B-A* 2 Some students wanted to investigate how the rate of photosynthesis in pond weed changed with light intensity. They did this by putting a lamp at different distances from some pond weed in a test tube. They counted the number of bubbles produced by the plant. Here is the data they collected.

Distance from lamp in cm	5	10	15	20	25	30
Number of bubbles per minute	124	88	64	42	32	16

a) Draw a graph of the number of bubbles per minute against the distance from the lamp. Join your points using straight lines.

(3 marks)

> If you are supposed to plot a line of best fit then you will be asked for it in the question.

b) Use your graph to find the number of bubbles you would expect in 1 minute if the lamp was placed 12 cm from the pond weed.

....

(1 mark)

c) Describe the relationship between light intensity and rate of photosynthesis.

....

....

(2 marks)

Limiting factors

B-A* 1 a) Name three factors that influence the rate of photosynthesis.

....

....

....

(3 marks)

b) Write a word equation for photosynthesis.

....

....

(2 marks)

C-A* 2 The graph shows how the rate of photosynthesis changes with light intensity. The data shows the rate at three different concentrations of carbon dioxide.

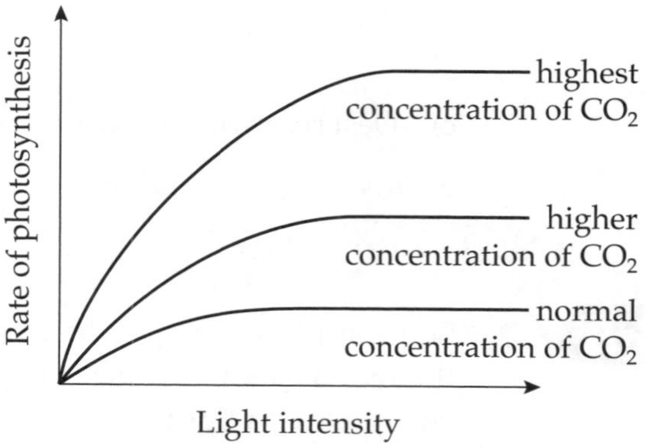

a) Describe how increasing the concentration of carbon dioxide changes the rate of photosynthesis.

....

(1 mark)

Guided b) Explain why each line on the graph levels off.

The rate reaches a .... This is because another factor

.... the rate.

(2 marks)

c) Explain how the rate of photosynthesis could be increased further.

You could increase the .... as this would make

photosynthesis happen ....

(2 marks)

B-A*
EXAM ALERT
3 A farmer wants to increase the rate of growth of some strawberry plants. He changes the temperature of his greenhouse from 15°C to 25°C and notices that the plants grow more quickly. The plants grow at the same speed at 35°C, but do not grow at all at 45°C. The farmer knows that photosynthesis uses enzymes. Explain why the growth of the plants changes in this way.

Students have struggled with exam questions similar to this – **be prepared!** ResultsPlus

If you are asked to explain something make sure you do explain rather than describe.

....

....

....

....

(4 marks)

Water transport

D-B

⟩**Guided**⟩

1   Plants take up water from the soil using one part of the plant. They use a different part of the plant to make sugars. Water and sugars need to be transported to all parts of the plant.

    a)   Name the part of the plant where **i)** water is taken up, **ii)** sugars are made.

       i)   Water is taken up by the ....

       ii)   Sugars are made in the ....

                                                          (2 marks)

    b)   Name the vessels that are used to transport water and sugars in plants.

       Water is transported in the ....

       Sugars are transported in the ....

                                                           (2 marks)

B-A*

2   A student set up the following experiment to investigate transpiration.

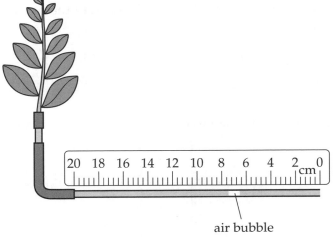

air bubble

    a)   What is meant by the term 'transpiration'?

       ....

       ....

                                                           (2 marks)

    b)   State which part of the plant regulates the rate of transpiration.

       ....

                                                           (1 mark)

    c)   Explain what happens to the air bubble if: | Remember that in an 'explain' question you need to say *what* happens and *why*.

       i)   a fan is started in front of the plant

       ....

       ....

                                                           (2 marks)

       ii)   the underside of the leaves of the plant are covered with grease.

       ....

       ....

                                                           (2 marks)

Osmosis

D-B   **1**   A student was investigating osmosis. She cut three pieces of the same size from a potato. She put one piece of potato into some distilled water, one piece into a weak sugar solution and the last piece into a strong sugar solution.

Guided   **a)**   Give a definition of the term **osmosis**.

> Make sure you use the terms 'water', 'partially permeable membrane' and 'movement' in your definition.

Osmosis is the movement of ....

across a .... from areas of

.... concentration to areas of .... concentration of water.

(3 marks)

b)   Describe why it is important that the three pieces of potato are the same size.

....

(1 mark)

c)   At the end of the experiment, the piece of potato in the weak sugar solution had not changed in length. Describe how the sizes of the other two pieces of potato would have changed.

....

....

(2 marks)

B-A*   **2**   This apparatus can be used to model the process of osmosis in cells.

When the experiment is left for several hours, the level of liquid in the tube rises.

a)   Describe what is meant by the term partially permeable.

....

(1 mark)

b)   Explain why the level of liquid in the tube rises.

....

....

(2 marks)

c)   Osmosis takes place in the roots of plants. Describe how root hair cells are adapted to carry out osmosis.

....

....

(2 marks)

Organisms and the environment

D-B 1 Most ants come out to find their food at night time. A student wants to find out where the ants feed in his garden. He decides to investigate the numbers of ants on the grass, under a tree and in a flower bed.

   a) Explain which technique would be best to use to collect the ants at night. Give a reason for your answer.

   ....

   ....

                                                   (2 marks)

   b) Describe how the student would make sure that his investigation was reliable.

   ....

   ....

      (2 marks)

   c) He wants to present his results to his teacher. Suggest a method he could use.

   ....

      (1 mark)

D-B 2 Give reasons why pooters are usually used to collect small insects.

Guided

> In this question, think about the alternative collection methods, and therefore give reasons why pooters are better than the other methods you know about.

Pooters are used because .... to the insects, unlike a method like sweep nets. Pooters are better for collecting small insects than a pitfall trap, as larger insects caught in a pitfall trap might .... the smaller ones.

      (2 marks)

B-A* 3 A student is investigating the number of earthworms in a field. The field measures 100 m by 25 m. She uses a quadrat that has an area of 1 m². She throws the quadrat four times onto different parts of the field. The table shows the numbers of earthworms she counts in each quadrat.

Quadrat number	1	2	3	4
Number of earthworms	24	17	31	28

   a) Calculate the mean number of worms found in the quadrats.

      Mean number of worms ....

      (1 mark)

   b) Calculate the area of the field.

      Area .... m²

      (1 mark)

   c) Estimate the population size of earthworms in the field.

      Population size ....

      (2 marks)

Biology extended writing 3

The graph shows the breathing rate for an adult at rest, during exercise, and in the recovery period after exercise.

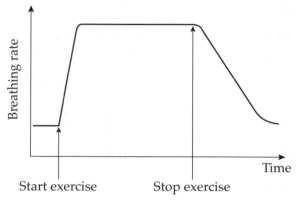

Explain the shape of this graph.

(6 marks)

You will be more successful in extended writing questions if you plan your answer before you start writing. Probably the best way to approach this question is to divide the graph into different sections and explain what is happening in each section in terms of breathing rate.

These sections are (1) the steep rising section after exercise starts, (2) the steady phase during exercise and (3) the falling section after exercise finishes.

Here are some questions that you might like to think about when constructing your answer:

- Which gases are useful in the air we breathe in?
- Why does breathing rate increase when exercise starts?
- Why does the breathing rate reach a maximum level?
- What happens in cells when exercise continues at the maximum breathing rate?
- Why does the breathing rate not return to normal more quickly after exercise stops?

....

....

....

....

....

....

....

....

....

....

....

Fossils and evolution

D-B

〉Guided〉

1   The diagram shows some fossil remains of ancestors of a modern animal.

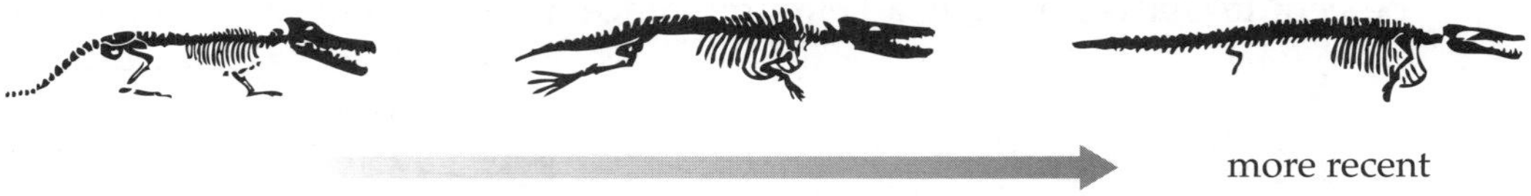

more recent

a)   Describe how the species of animal making these fossils changed over time.

The skull became ....

The back legs became .... **(2 marks)**

b)   The changes in these fossils give evidence for a process. What is this process called?
Put a cross (☒) in the box next to your answer.

☐ **A** evolution   ☐ **B** extinction   ☐ **C** growth   ☐ **D** selective breeding

(1 mark)

D-B

2   There are many gaps in the fossil record. One reason for this is that not all fossils have been found. Explain one other reason why the fossil record is not complete.

....

....

(2 marks)

B-A*

3   The diagram shows an X-ray image of a bat. The bat is a mammal that can fly.

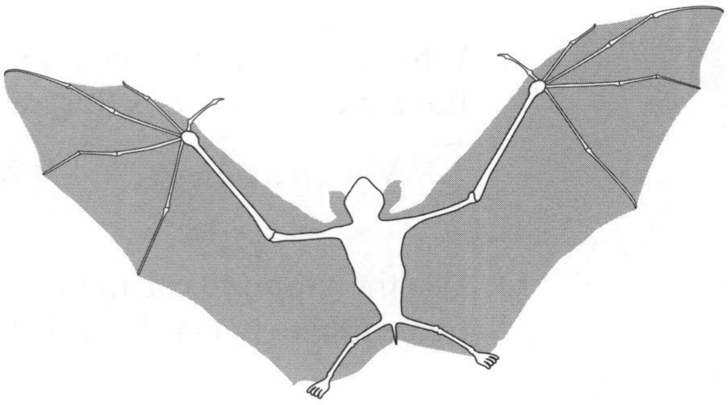

a)   State one similarity and one difference between the limb in bats and humans.

....

....

....

(2 marks)

b)   In his book *On the Origin of Species*, Charles Darwin wrote:

What could be more curious than that the hand of man formed for grasping, that of a mole, for digging and the paddle of a porpoise should all include similar bones and in the same relative positions?

Explain how the structure of the limbs of vertebrates, both in living mammals and in fossils, provides evidence for evolution.

> Use the information in the question to help you. Darwin compares the limbs of different mammals – what do these mammalian limbs have in common? Is this pattern also seen in fossils? What does it tell us about the ancestors of modern mammals?

....

....

....

(3 marks)

Had a go ☐   Nearly there ☐   Nailed it! ☐

Growth

D-B

Guided

1   A midwife will measure the growth of a baby in different ways. The graph shows some percentile charts for the head circumference measurement for young children.

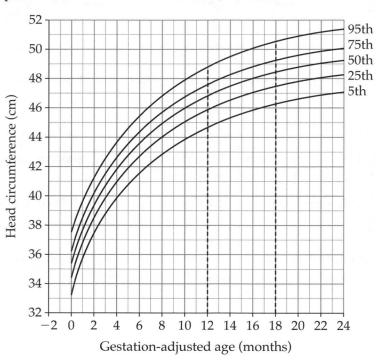

> Graphs like this sometimes look complicated – but remember that the curves are all labelled, so you can see what each one refers to.

> Note that guidelines have been put in to help you answer this part of this question. These help you to show how you get the reading for both measurements from the graph – you can then subtract one number from the other to get the final answer.

a) Which percentile curve on the graph represents the average readings for a baby? Put a cross in the box (☒) next to your answer.

☐ **A** 5th percentile   ☐ **B** 25th percentile   ☐ **C** 50th percentile   ☐ **D** 75th percentile
(1 mark)

b) Use the graph to calculate the change in head circumference for a baby in the 25th percentile between 12 and 18 months old.

Change in circumference .... cm
(2 marks)

D-B

2   Growth in seedlings can be investigated by measuring the mass of seedlings of different ages.

a) One seedling increased in mass from 12.75 g to 15.35 g over a period of 7 days. Calculate the percentage increase in mass for this seeding.

Percentage increase .... %
(2 marks)

b) Describe one other way you could measure the growth of the seedlings.

....

....
(2 marks)

Growth of plants and animals

D-B

> **Guided**

1 Plants and animals grow in different ways.

Remember that there are three different processes involved in growth and development: cell differentiation, cell division and cell elongation. You should know what each means and how it takes place.

a) Describe where cell division takes place during the growth of plants.

In plants, cell division happens at the .... of the ....

(2 marks)

b) Describe how animals increase in size during growth.

The type of cell division used for growth is .... This

continues until they ....

(2 marks)

D-B

2 Plants produce new cells through cell division.

a) Name the process of cell division that occurs in most plant cells.

....

(1 mark)

b) Plants can grow by producing new cells. Describe one other way that plants grow.

....

....

(2 marks)

B-A*

3 Growth in animals happens over a particular period of the animal's lifespan. Growth happens through cell division and when specialised cells in the animal differentiate.

a) Name the special cells in animals that can differentiate.

....

(1 mark)

b) Explain what is meant by the term **differentiate**.

....

....

(2 marks)

c) Animals stop growing when they reach adulthood. Suggest why cell division continues to happen in adult animals.

....

(1 mark)

d) If a human loses an arm, it does not regrow; but a plant will regrow a leaf if one is lost. Explain why humans and plants show this difference in their growth.

....

....

....

(2 marks)

Blood

D-B   **1**   Blood contains a large number of red blood cells.

    a)   Name the cell structure, normally found in animal cells, that is missing in red blood cells.

    ....

                                                                     (1 mark)

    b)   Name the compound in red blood cells that gives them their colour.

    ....

                                                                     (1 mark)

> **Guided**   **c)**   Describe two ways in which red blood cells are adapted to carry out their function.

> Think about features of a red blood cell … then consider the jobs that the red blood cells do – all you then have to do is to match a feature to the job! The table will help you structure your answer.

Feature	Function

                                                                     (4 marks)

D-B   **2**   The plasma carries materials around the body. Name a waste material carried by the plasma, and state where it is carried to.

    ....

    ....

                                                                       (2 marks)

B-A*   **3**   Platelets are small cell fragments in the blood. Describe the role of platelets.

    ....

    ....

    ....

                                                                     (3 marks)

B-A*   **4**   White blood cells usually make up about 1% of the blood.

    a)   State one reason that the number of white blood cells could increase in the blood.

    ....

                                                                       (1 mark)

    b)   Describe the role of white blood cells.

    ....

    ....

    ....

                                                                       (3 marks)

The heart

D–B

> **Guided**

1 The heart is connected to four major blood vessels. Describe where each vessel carries blood. The first one has been done for you.

aorta   carries blood from heart to body

pulmonary artery   carries blood from .... to ....

pulmonary vein   carries blood from .... to ....

vena cava   carries blood from .... to ....

(4 marks)

D–B

2 The human heart is divided into two sides. Each side of the heart contains two chambers.

a) Name the two chambers found on the right-hand side of the heart.

....

....

(2 marks)

b) Describe how the composition of the blood is different in the two sides of the heart.

> Think about how the oxygen levels vary on the different sides of the heart.

....

....

(2 marks)

B–A*

3 The diagram shows a section through the human heart.

> Remember that the heart is drawn and labelled as if you are looking at the heart in someone's body. So the right side of the heart is actually on the left side of the page!

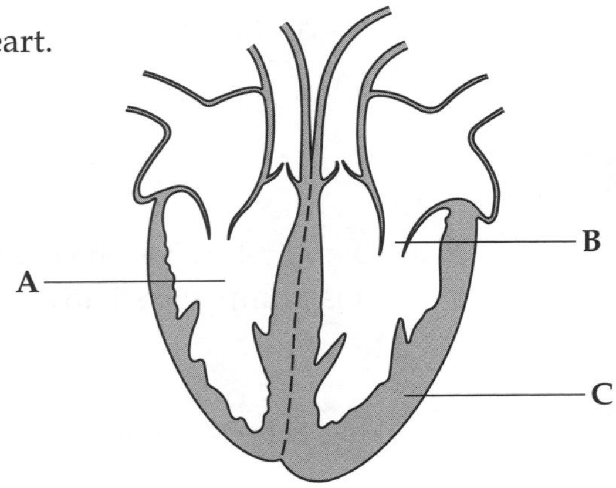

a) Name the part of the heart labelled A.

....

(1 mark)

b) Name the role of the part of the heart labelled B.

....

....

(2 marks)

c) Explain why the muscle at C needs to be thicker than on the other side of the heart.

....

....

....

(3 marks)

The circulatory system

D-B 1 The circulatory system is an organ system. Describe the organisation of this system in terms of organs and tissues.

....

....

....

(3 marks)

D-B 2 Rewrite the following sentences, correcting the error in each.

> In each case, you need to insert the correct information in the sentence.

Guided

   a) Both arteries leaving the heart carry oxygenated blood.

      The aorta carries oxygenated blood away from the heart but the pulmonary artery does not.

   b) The vena cava takes blood from the heart to the body.

....

(1 mark)

   c) The circulatory system is made up of the arteries, veins and capillaries only.

....

(1 mark)

C-A 3 In humans, oxygenated blood is carried from the heart to the body, and deoxygenated blood returns to the heart.

   a) Other than the level of oxygen, describe one difference in the blood returning from the heart to the body.

....

....

(2 marks)

   b) Blood returns to the heart from the hand. Describe the journey taken by this blood until it is pumped back towards the hand.

....

....

....

....

(4 marks)

   c) Suggest why capillaries have thin walls.

....

....

(2 marks)

B-A* 4 Bacteria and other microorganisms do not have a circulatory system. Suggest why they do not need a circulatory system.

....

....

(2 marks)

The digestive system

D-B 1 Rice and pasta contain starch.

a) Name the enzyme that breaks down starch. Put a cross in the box (☒) next to your answer.

☐ **A** amylase   ☐ **B** lipase   ☐ **C** protease   ☐ **D** starchase

(1 mark)

b) This enzyme digests starch in two different areas of the digestive system.
Name these two parts.

.... and .... (2 marks)

c) Explain why it is important for the body to digest molecules such as starch.

....

....

(2 marks)

D-B 2 Describe how food is moved from the mouth to the stomach.

‹Guided›

When food is swallowed it moves into a tube called the o... The food

is moved because of... contracting in waves. This process is called

.... (3 marks)

B-A* 3 The pancreas and the gall bladder are organs in the digestive system.

a) The pancreas produces proteases. Explain the function of a protease.

....

....

(2 marks)

b) The gall bladder stores a substance used in digestion.

i) Name this substance.

.... (1 mark)

ii) Where is this substance produced before being stored in the gall bladder?

Take care here – many candidates get confused about where this substance is produced.
As the question says, it is only stored in the gall bladder, it is not made there.

.... (1 mark)

c) The substance stored in the gall bladder has two roles. One of these is to emulsify fats.

i) Explain the importance of emulsification.

....

....

(2 marks)

ii) Explain the other function of this substance and why it is necessary.

....

....

....

(3 marks)

Villi

D-B
Guided

1 The products of digestion are absorbed in the small intestine. For each food molecule, name the enzyme that breaks it down and the products of digestion.

> For each of the three different food molecules in the diet, you need to know the type (and name) of the enzyme that breaks them down and the products formed.

Molecule broken down	Enzyme	Products formed
	carbohydrase/amylase	simple sugars
		amino acids
fat		.... and ....

(3 marks)

D-B

2 The small intestine is adapted to absorb food molecules produced through digestion.

a) Name the structures in the small intestine that help absorb food molecules.

....

(1 mark)

b) Describe the process that allows these molecules to pass from the small intestine into the blood.

....

....

(2 marks)

c) Explain why digestion is important to allow absorption to happen quickly.

....

....

(2 marks)

B-A*

3 Crohn's disease is a condition that causes inflammation of the small intestine. People with Crohn's disease often have weight loss as a symptom. Explain why.

....

....

....

(3 marks)

B-A*

4 Explain how the villi in the small intestine are adapted for the rapid, efficient absorption of the products of digestion.

....

....

....

(3 marks)

Probiotics and prebiotics

1 Plant statins are a form of stanol esters that are claimed to lower cholesterol in the blood. A study was carried out to test this idea. 200 people took part in the trial. 100 people were given statins and the other 100 people were not. All the people in the trial were given advice on how to lower cholesterol in their diet.

The graph shows the cholesterol levels in the two groups of people over the 13 weeks of the study.

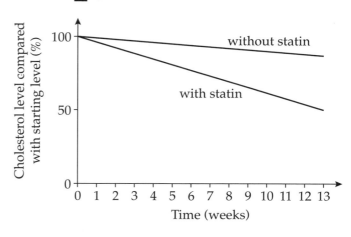

a) Explain why the study included a group of patients who did not take the plant statins.

....

....

(2 marks)

b) Describe the effect of plant statins on the level of cholesterol in the blood.

> You will need to use information from the graph to help you to answer this question. You should say what effect the graph shows that statins have on cholesterol levels and compare this with the other group.

The effect of diet alone is to .... cholesterol. If statins are also taken,

the level of cholesterol becomes ...., and the effect is

.... than diet alone.

(3 marks)

2 Many people are keen to take prebiotic and probiotic foods to improve their health.

a) Name one substance that is a probiotic.

.... **(1 mark)**

b) Describe how the claimed benefits of probiotics can be evaluated.

....

....

....

(3 marks)

3 A survey showed that 5% of women have a condition called irritable bowel syndrome (IBS). The manufacturers of a yoghurt claimed that eating the yoghurt helped prevent IBS. In a trial, 750 women selected at random ate the yoghurt as part of their diet. 35 of the women reported symptoms of IBS. Use this information to evaluate the effectiveness of this yoghurt in preventing IBS.

....

....

....

(3 marks)

Biology extended writing 4

One job of a midwife is to check that a baby is developing normally. She does this by taking measurements and comparing these with graphs like the one shown.

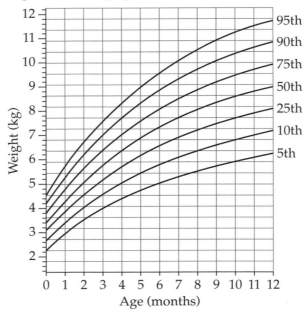

Explain how a midwife would take measurements and use this graph to check the development of a 6-month-old baby.

(6 marks)

You will be more successful in extended writing questions if you plan your answer before you start writing. In questions that involve data or graphs, you should show that you can read and use the information presented. In this case, your answer will be improved by using the data in the graph to illustrate your answer.

You might like to consider the following questions:

- What is being measured in this graph?
- How would the midwife make this measurement?
- What do the lines on this graph show?
- What results would be considered 'normal'?
- Would the midwife use the result at 6 months by itself to work out if growth was normal?

Remember to use some data from the graph to illustrate your answer.

....

....

....

....

....

....

....

Biology extended writing 5

Human circulation is often described as a 'double circulatory system'. One feature of this system is that oxygenated and deoxygenated blood are kept separate from each other in the heart.

Explain how the flow of blood through the heart prevents oxygenated and deoxygenated blood from mixing.

(6 marks)

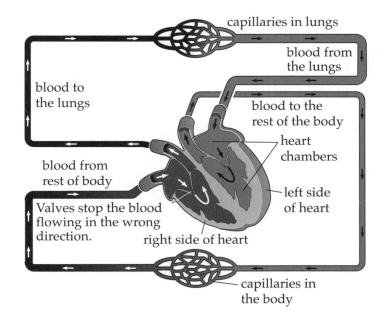

capillaries in lungs

blood from the lungs

blood to the lungs

blood to the rest of the body

heart chambers

left side of heart

blood from rest of body

right side of heart

Valves stop the blood flowing in the wrong direction.

capillaries in the body

You will be more successful with extended writing questions if you plan your answer before you start writing.

You may not have heard of the term 'double circulation', so use the diagram to help you understand what this means. However, to answer the question, you are simply being asked to say how the heart is structured to keep the blood on the two sides separate. So, you just need to say how the blood moves from the heart to the lungs and the body, and back.

Pick a part of the heart to start your answer – in this case it's probably easiest to start with the oxygenated blood coming into the heart.

To help you get your answer in the right order think about:

- where the oxygenated blood comes from, and which vessel brings it to the heart
- how the oxygenated blood moves through the heart
- how the heart is designed to make sure the blood doesn't cross over in the heart
- where deoxygenated blood comes from, and which vessel brings it to the heart
- how the deoxygenated blood moves through the heart.

Don't forget to be clear about the left and right sides of the heart.

....

....

....

....

....

....

....

....

....

....

Structure of the atom

> Remember that *atoms* are neutral. If they gain or lose an electron they become *ions*.

D-C   1   Explain why atoms are neutral and have no overall charge.

....

....

(2 marks)

D-C   2   Explain how to calculate the mass number of an element that contains four protons, four neutrons and four electrons.

....

....

....

(3 marks)

C-A   3   One atom of an element has 10 protons, 10 electrons and 10 neutrons. Which row of the table represents an atom of an isotope of this element? Put a cross (☒) in the box next to your answer.

	Protons	Electrons	Neutrons
☐ A	10	12	10
☐ B	10	10	12
☐ C	12	10	10
☐ D	12	12	12

(1 mark)

B-A*   4   There are two stable isotopes of chlorine: chlorine-35 and chlorine-37. The relative abundance of chlorine-35 (which has a relative mass of 35) in a sample is 75.8%. Show that the relative atomic mass of chlorine is 35.5.

Guided

the relative abundance of chlorine-37 is ....%.

$$\text{relative atomic mass} = \frac{35 \times 75.8 + 37 \times \ldots\ldots\ldots}{100}$$

$$= \frac{2653 + \ldots\ldots\ldots}{100} =$$

> The values for abundance are given to 3 significant figures, so your answer cannot be more accurate than three significant figures.

Relative atomic mass ....

(3 marks)

B-A*   5   There are two stable isotopes of copper: copper-63 and copper-65. The relative abundance of copper-63 is 69%. Calculate the relative atomic mass of copper.

Relative atomic mass ....

(3 marks)

The modern periodic table

D-C

1 Put ticks in the boxes to show whether each description is for a group or for a period.

Description	Group	Period
a vertical column is a	✓	
a horizontal row is a		
aluminium, sodium and chlorine are in the same		
beryllium, magnesium and calcium are in the same		
elements with similar properties are in the same		

> The periodic table on page 122 will help you with these questions.

(5 marks)

D-C

2 Today, the elements in the periodic table are arranged in order of their increasing atomic number.

a) State the symbol for the element with two more protons in its nucleus than

carbon: ....

(1 mark)

b) State the symbol for the element with two more electrons in its atom than

lithium: ....

(1 mark)

D-B

3 The relative atomic mass of the element boron is 11. It is the fifth element in the periodic table. Explain what this information tells us about what the boron atom contains.

....

....

(2 marks)

B-A*

4 Mendeleev arranged the 60 or so elements known at the time in order of increasing atomic mass, as measured by experiment. He found this sequence produced a repeating pattern in their chemical properties. Some elements did not exactly fit the pattern unless their positions in the sequence were swapped. For example, he placed tellurium before iodine although its atomic mass is greater than iodine.

a) In the modern periodic table (page 122), tellurium is also placed before iodine. Explain why tellurium is placed before iodine in the modern periodic table.

....

....

....

(3 marks)

b) Mendeleev listed elements in order of increasing atomic mass, except for iodine and tellurium. Suggest why Mendeleev broke the 'sequence rule' for these two elements.

....

....

....

(3 marks)

Had a go ☐   Nearly there ☐   Nailed it! ☐

Electron shells

D-C 1 An element has an atomic number of 8. What is its electronic configuration? Put a cross (☒) in the box next to your answer.

☐ **A** 8   ☐ **C** 2.6

☐ **B** 4.4   ☐ **D** 2.4.2

> Remember how the group number and period number relate to the electronic structure.

(1 mark)

D-C
⟩Guided⟩

2 **a)** An atom, Y, has 13 electrons. Draw a diagram to show its electronic configuration.

> When you are drawing electronic configurations it is usual to group the electrons in some of the shells in pairs, but the important thing is to make sure that there are the correct number of electrons in each shell.

(3 marks)

b) State the name of the element: ....

(1 mark)

> Refer to the periodic table on page 122 to find information about elements.

D-C 3 Draw a diagram to show the electronic configuration of carbon.

(3 marks)

D-C 4 State the electronic configuration of atom Z ....

(1 mark)

B-A* 5 The single electron in the outer shell of a sodium atom can be removed fairly easily. When it is removed, the part left behind is called a sodium **ion**. Explain how the electronic configuration of a sodium ion is like that of an atom of a different element.

> This question is designed to help you take your thinking a bit further, as it contains useful information. Make sure you use the information to help you answer the question.

....

....

(2 marks)

Ions

1 Use the periodic table to help you to write down the symbols for the ions formed by the following elements.

a) calcium ....Ca²⁺..........

b) fluorine ....

c) lithium ....

d) sulfur ....

Students have struggled with exam questions similar to this in the past – **be prepared!**

Remember that metal atoms lose one, two or three electrons to form positive ions and non-metal atoms gain one or more electrons to become negative ions.

(4 marks)

2 a) Write the electronic configuration of the ion shown in the diagram ....

(1 mark)

b) Is this an anion or a cation? ....

(1 mark)

3 a) The diagram shows a chloride ion. Explain how such ions are formed.

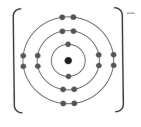

....

....

(2 marks)

b) Magnesium reacts with oxygen to form magnesium oxide. Magnesium has an atomic number of 12 and oxygen has an atomic number of 8. Draw a diagram to show how the electrons are arranged in the ions found in magnesium oxide.

(3 marks)

4 Describe the relationship between the ion K⁺, the ion Cl⁻ and the atom Ar.

....

....

(2 marks)

41

Ionic compounds

B-D   1   Explain why the hydroxide ion in $Ca(OH)_2$ is put in brackets while the chloride ion in $CaCl_2$ does not need brackets.

....

....

(2 marks)

D-B   2   The tables show the charges on different ions.

Guided

Positive ions		Charge
aluminium	Al^{3+}	3+
calcium	Ca^{2+}	2+
copper	Cu^{2+}	2+
iron (III)	Fe^{3+}	3+
magnesium	Mg^{2+}	2+
sodium	Na^+	1+
ammonium	$NH_4{}^+$	1+

Negative ions		Charge
bromide	Br^-	1−
carbonate	$CO_3{}^{2-}$	2−
chloride	Cl^-	1−
iodide	I^-	1−
oxide	O^{2-}	2−
sulfate	$SO_4{}^{2-}$	2−
hydroxide	OH^-	1−
nitrate	$NO_3{}^-$	1−

Write the formula for each of these compounds.

magnesium bromide   ......$MgBr_2$......   sodium iodide ....

calcium sulfate ....   copper carbonate ....

aluminium chloride ....   sodium nitrate ....

(6 marks)

B-A*   3   Write the formula of each of these compounds.

calcium hydroxide ....   iron (III) oxide ....

sodium sulfate ....   copper nitrate ....

aluminium sulfate ....   ammonium carbonate ....

(6 marks)

Properties of ionic compounds

1 For each substance, put a tick (✓) in the boxes to show whether it is soluble or insoluble in water.

Chemical	Soluble	Insoluble
sodium chloride	✓	
silver chloride		
magnesium hydroxide		
barium chloride		
barium carbonate		

> You need to learn the rules for which salts are soluble in water and which are insoluble in water.

(5 marks)

EXAM ALERT

2 Complete the sentence by putting a cross (☒) in the box next to your answer.

Ionic substances:

☐ **A**   are usually gases at 0°C.

☐ **B**   usually have a low boiling point.

☐ **C**   are solids at room temperature.

☐ **D**   have higher melting points than boiling points.

> Students have struggled with exam questions similar to this in the past – **be prepared!**   ResultsPlus

> Remember that ionic compounds have high melting and boiling points because of strong electrostatic forces between oppositely charged ions.

(1 mark)

3 Two students made statements about ionic substances.

Statement 1: Ionic substances are insulators except in solution.

Statement 2: Ionic substances conduct electricity as solids, liquids and gases.

Which of these statements is/are correct? Put a cross (☒) next to your answer.

☐ **A**   statement 1 only   ☐ **B**   statement 2 only

☐ **C**   both statements 1 and 2   ☐ **D**   neither

(1 mark)

4 A concentrated solution of sodium chloride in water conducts electricity well. Sodium chloride crystals do not conduct electricity. Both the solution and the solid contain ions.

Explain the difference between the electrical properties of the solution and the crystals.

....

....

....

(2 marks)

Precipitates

D-C   1   The table shows some properties of four ionic substances.

Chemical	Formula	Colour of crystals	Is it soluble?
lead iodide	PbI_2	yellow	no
lead nitrate	$Pb(NO_3)_2$	white	yes
potassium iodide	KI	white	yes
potassium nitrate	KNO_3	white	yes

When lead nitrate solution reacts with potassium iodide solution, the products are potassium nitrate and lead iodide.

Guided   **a)**   Write the balanced equation for the reaction between lead nitrate and potassium iodide. Give the state symbols.

> This is a guided question, so some of the answer has been done for you, but the equation has to be balanced and there are no state symbols yet.

> In a balanced equation, there are the same number of each type of atom on each side of the equation. Make sure you understand how to do this.

$Pb(NO_3)_2$ ( ) + ... KI ( ) → PbI_2 ( ) + ... KNO_3 ( )   **(3 marks)**

b)   A technician is asked to purify the lead iodide from a mixture of powders. The mixture contains potassium iodide and lead nitrate. He shakes the mixture in a test tube with some water. Then, he places the test tube in a rack.

i)   Describe what he can **see** after he adds the water to the powder.

....

(1 mark)

ii)   Describe how he can continue to produce a pure, dry sample of lead iodide.

....

....

....

(3 marks)

B-A*   2   A barium salt is given as a 'barium meal'. X-ray photographs are taken as the 'meal' passes through the digestive system. Barium absorbs X-rays but is also toxic. Use this information and your knowledge of solubilities to explain why barium sulfate is used in preference to barium nitrate.

....

....

....

....

(4 marks)

B-A*   3   When sodium hydroxide (NaOH) solution is added to copper sulfate ($CuSO_4$) solution, a pale blue precipitate is formed with a colourless solution.

Complete the balanced equation for the reaction, giving state symbols.

.... → $Cu(OH)_2$ ( ) + Na_2SO_4 ( )   **(2 marks)**

Ion tests

D-C

⟩**Guided**⟩

1 Describe the test to show that a solution contains carbonate ions.

Add a few drops of .... to the sample. Test the gas given off with

.... which turns .... with a carbonate.

(3 marks)

D-C

2 **a)** Describe how to carry out a flame test for sodium ions.

....

....

....

(3 marks)

b) You are given a white powder. Describe how you could confirm that it contained calcium ions.

....

....

(2 marks)

B-A*

EXAM ALERT

3 A student tested two white powders, P and Q. Each powder contained a single compound. Here are some of her observations:

- A flame test with P gives a bright yellow flame.
- Both powders dissolve in water and each makes a colourless solution.
- When a little nitric acid is added to some of solution Q, followed by a few drops of silver nitrate solution, a white precipitate forms.
- When some of solution P is mixed with some of solution Q, a white precipitate forms.
- When some of this precipitate is washed and dried, a flame test on it gives a red flame.

Students have struggled with exam questions similar to this in the past – **be prepared!**   Results**Plus**

If you are asked to describe the test for a substance, you need to say how to carry out the test *and* what you would see if the substance is the one you expect.

a) State which metal ions are in P and Q.

....

....

(2 marks)

b) Which non-metal ion is present in Q?

....

(1 mark)

c) Explain why there are several possible compositions of powder Q.

....

....

(2 marks)

Chemistry extended writing 1

Barium sulfate is an insoluble compound. It is used in medicine because it is opaque to X-rays. This is useful if doctors want to take an X-ray of the digestive system.

Describe how you could make a pure, dry sample of barium sulfate in the laboratory from two soluble salts. Your method should include an equation for the reaction.

(6 marks)

> You will be more successful in extended writing questions if you plan your answer before you start writing.
>
> This question asks you to describe a method for an experiment. You need to think about the starting materials needed for the reaction as well as the steps involved.
>
> The very first sentence gives us the key word – **insoluble.** You should remember that insoluble salts are made from mixing together soluble salts. So you need to think of two salts: a soluble barium salt and a soluble sulfate.
>
> (If you need a clue, remember that all nitrates are soluble, and all sodium salts are soluble.)
>
> Remember to describe how you will carry out the reaction, and how you will collect the salt. The next clues you have are the words **pure** and **dry**. These give you a clue about what steps to take after making the salt.
>
> Last, don't forget the **equation** – ideally this should be a balanced symbol equation.
>
> You will get better marks on this extended writing question if you give a detailed method with steps in the right order, and use a balanced equation.

....
....
....
....
....
....
....
....
....
....
....
....
....
....
....
....
....

Covalent bonds

The periodic table on page 122 tells you what the atomic number is for each element and therefore how many electrons there are in each atom. The exam paper will include a periodic table.

1   Draw the dot and cross diagram to show the arrangement of electrons in a molecule of hydrogen fluoride (atomic number: hydrogen = 1, fluorine = 9).

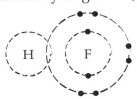

(3 marks)

Students have struggled with exam questions similar to this in the past – **be prepared!**

Although the electrons from different elements are not really any different it is easier to see which electrons come from each atom if you draw them as dots or crosses. Here it might be easier to draw the electrons from hydrogen as crosses.

2   Draw the dot and cross diagram for a methane molecule, CH_4 (atomic number: hydrogen = 1, carbon = 6).

(3 marks)

3   The electronic configuration of chlorine is 2.8.7. Explain why the formula for a chlorine molecule is Cl_2.

....

....

(2 marks)

4   The structure of an ethene molecule is shown. Draw the dot and cross diagram for an ethene (C_2H_4) molecule.

$$H\diagdown \diagup H$$
$$C=C$$
$$H\diagup \diagdown H$$

(4 marks)

5   One oxygen atom combines with two hydrogen atoms to form a molecule of water but two oxygen atoms need to combine with one carbon atom to form a molecule of carbon dioxide. Explain why there is only one atom of oxygen in a water molecule but two in a carbon dioxide molecule. You may draw diagrams to help your answer.

....

....

....

....

(4 marks)

Covalent substances

D-C 1 a) State one property of diamond that is typical of other giant molecular covalent substances.

....

(1 mark)

> **Guided**

b) Compare the bonding in diamond with the bonding in graphite.

In diamond each carbon atom is bonded to ....

In graphite each carbon atom is bonded to ....

(2 marks)

D-C 2 a) Compare the structures of simple molecular covalent substances and giant molecular covalent substances.

....

....

(2 marks)

EXAM ALERT

b) Compare the strength of the forces holding together molecules in a simple molecular covalent substance and a giant molecular covalent substance.

....

....

....

....

| Students have struggled with exam questions similar to this in the past – **be prepared!** ResultsPlus |
| Remember, bonds between atoms in a covalent substance are always strong. |

(3 marks)

D-C 3 Complete the table, which compares the general properties of simple molecular covalent substances and giant molecular covalent substances.

Property	Simple molecular covalent substance	Giant molecular covalent substance
conducting electricity		poor (except for graphite)
boiling point	low	
melting point		

(4 marks)

B-A* 4 Explain why graphite and diamond both have very high melting points.

....

....

(2 marks)

B-A* 5 A third form of pure carbon was discovered in the 1980s. Fullerenes are made from carbon atoms joined by covalent bonds. The first fullerene to be discovered had 60 carbon atoms joined in a spherical shape. Suggest whether this fullerene is giant molecular or simple molecular covalent substance.

....

....

(2 marks)

Miscible or immiscible?

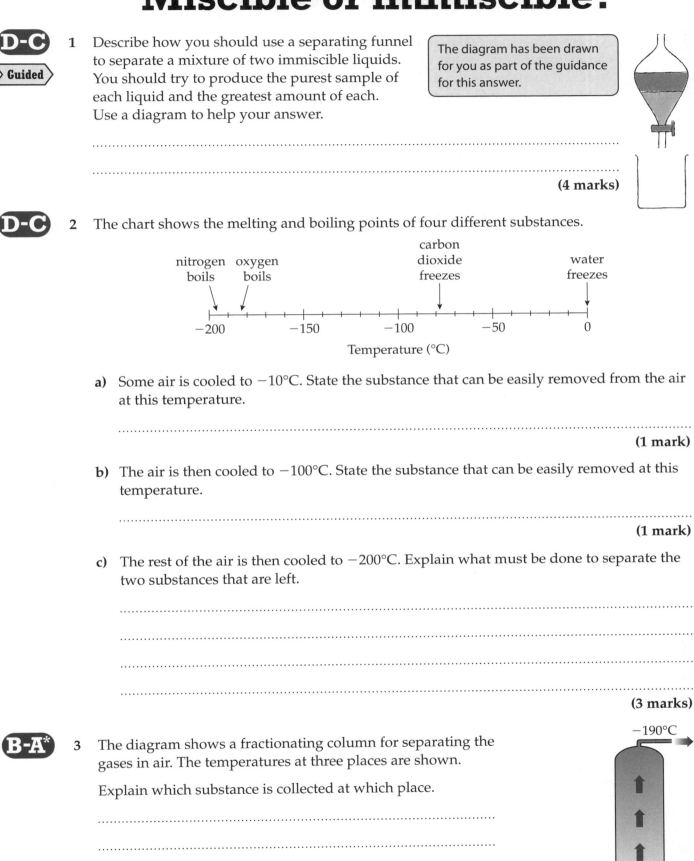

D-C

Guided

1   Describe how you should use a separating funnel to separate a mixture of two immiscible liquids. You should try to produce the purest sample of each liquid and the greatest amount of each. Use a diagram to help your answer.

The diagram has been drawn for you as part of the guidance for this answer.

....

....

(4 marks)

D-C

2   The chart shows the melting and boiling points of four different substances.

a)   Some air is cooled to −10°C. State the substance that can be easily removed from the air at this temperature.

....

(1 mark)

b)   The air is then cooled to −100°C. State the substance that can be easily removed at this temperature.

....

(1 mark)

c)   The rest of the air is then cooled to −200°C. Explain what must be done to separate the two substances that are left.

....

....

....

....

(3 marks)

B-A*

3   The diagram shows a fractionating column for separating the gases in air. The temperatures at three places are shown.

Explain which substance is collected at which place.

....

....

....

....

....

(3 marks)

49

Chromatography

D-C **1** A chemist checks for fake coins using chromatography. He reacts the sample coin with acid to make a solution. He then tests it with solutions made from known metals. The diagram shows the chromatogram he obtained.

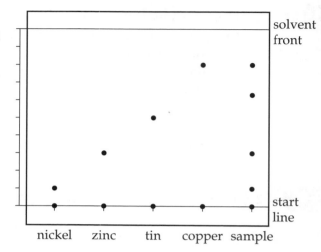

a) A student looks at these results and suggests that the sample coins contain more copper than tin. Explain why this conclusion cannot be drawn from the results.

....

....

....

(2 marks)

b) Nickel has a lower R_f value than copper. Compare the R_f values for copper, zinc and tin.

> You do not need to calculate them here – you can just compare what is on the diagram.

....

....

(2 marks)

c) A genuine coin should contain some of each of the metals shown. Give two reasons to explain whether the sample is real or whether it is a fake.

....

....

....

(3 marks)

D-C **2** The diagram shows a chromatogram of a dye. Calculate the R_f value of the dye.

Guided

$$R_f = \frac{\text{distance moved by compound}}{\text{distance moved by solvent}}$$

distance moved by compound .... cm

distance moved by solvent .... cm

$R_f = $ ....

> R_f values do not have a unit since they are a ratio.

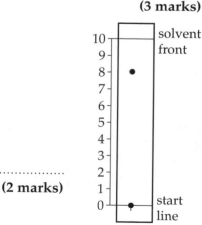

(2 marks)

B-A* **3** A scientist measured the R_f value for a coloured dye on a paper chromatogram. It was 0.6. The dye had moved 3 cm from its first position. How far had the solvent moved in the same time?

Distance .... cm

(2 marks)

Chemical classification 1

D-C 1 **a)** Name the type of substance that is made from millions of atoms covalently bonded together.

....

(1 mark)

> Read the question carefully to make sure you know if you are talking about atoms, ions or molecules.

b) Name two groups of substances that are usually solid at room temperature.

....

(1 mark)

c) State which group of substances conduct electricity when they are molten or in solution.

....

(1 mark)

d) State which type of substance generally has strong bonds between atoms in each molecule but weak forces between molecules.

....

(1 mark)

⟩Guided⟩ **e)** Describe the difference between giant and simple covalent structures.

In giant structures, millions of atoms are held together by strong bonds while in simple

covalent substances ....

(2 marks)

D-C 2 **a)** Explain how investigating the melting point of a substance can help you find out about its structure.

....

....

....

(3 marks)

b) Describe one property other than solubility or melting point that would allow you to decide whether a substance was an ionic or a giant molecular covalent substance.

....

....

(2 marks)

B-A* 3 Describe the differences in the bonding in ionic and covalent substances. You may draw a labelled diagram to help your answer.

....

....

(4 marks)

Chemical classification 2

D-C 1 A powder is found to be insoluble. Explain why this observation is not enough to identify the type of bonding found in the powder.

....

....

(2 marks)

D-C 2 **a)** Explain why the structure of a metal means that it can conduct electricity.

....

....

(2 marks)

b) Explain why the structure of giant ionic substances means that they do not conduct electricity when solid but might when dissolved in water or molten.

....

....

....

(3 marks)

D-C
Guided 3 Describe how you would test the electrical conductivity of a substance when it is solid or dissolved.

Put the sample in a beaker and test with an electric current that contains a bulb.

Test the sample in all three ....

The bulb will light if the substance ....

(3 marks)

B-A* 4 Explain, in terms of their structures, why graphite is a conductor of electricity, while diamond is not.

....

....

....

....

(4 marks)

Metals and bonding

D-C 1 Metals are malleable.

a) State what is meant by the term malleable.

....

(1 mark)

> **Guided**

b) Explain, with the help of the diagram, what happens when a metal is hit with a hammer.

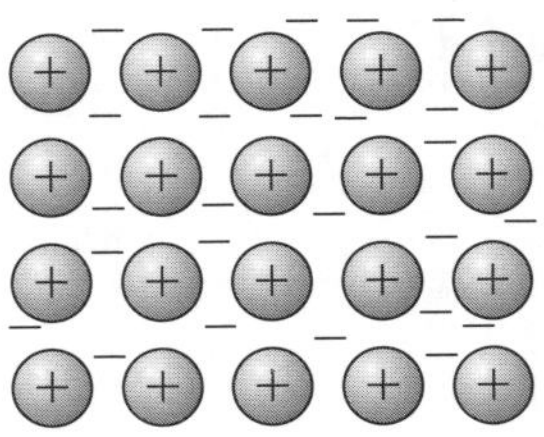

Before the metal is hit, the atoms are arranged in layers.

When the atoms are hit with a hammer they form a thinner

sheet because ....

(2 marks)

EXAM ALERT

Students have struggled with exam questions similar to this in the past – **be prepared!**   ResultsPlus

Make sure you understand how the structure of a metal is related to its properties.

D-C 2 The diagram above also shows the metal ions in a piece of metal held together by a sea of electrons.

a) The electrons are described as delocalised. State the meaning of the word delocalised.

....

(1 mark)

b) Use the diagram to help you to explain why metals conduct electricity.

....

....

(2 marks)

B-A* 3 The first diagram shows the arrangement of metal ions in a pure metal. The second diagram shows ions of two metals in an alloy.

Pure metal

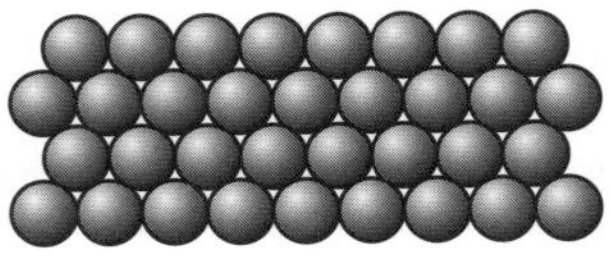

An alloy

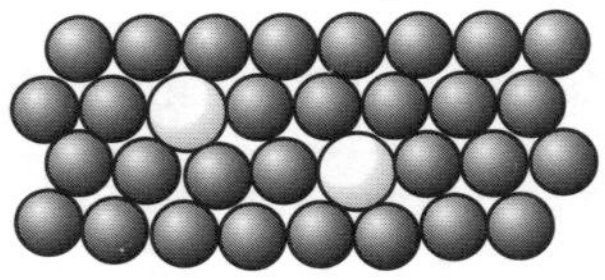

Compare the two diagrams to suggest why the malleability of a metal decreases when a small amount of a second metal is added.

....

....

(2 marks)

53

Alkali metals

D-C **1** The graph shows the boiling points of four alkali metals.

> Look at the boiling points of potassium and caesium to help you with question **1b**.

> Guided

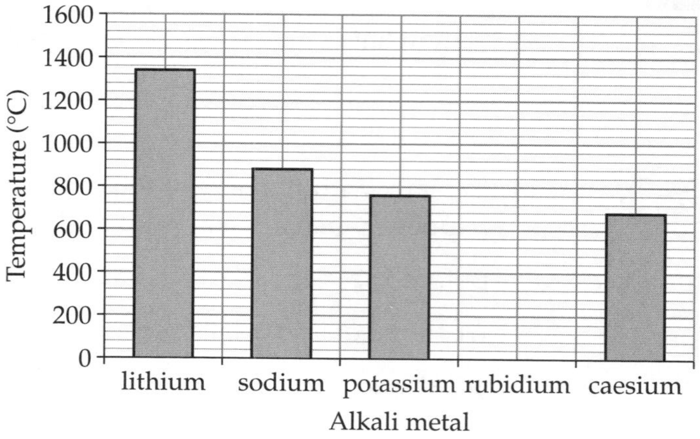

a) State the boiling points of sodium and lithium.

Sodium: ....*about 880°C*.............

Lithium: ....

(2 marks)

b) Estimate a value for the boiling point of rubidium: ....

(1 mark)

c) State how the boiling point of alkali metals changes with their position in the periodic table.

....

(1 mark)

D-C **2** **a)** Write a word equation for the reaction that occurs when potassium is dropped into water.

....

(1 mark)

b) Write a balanced equation for this reaction.

....

....

(3 marks)

B-A* **3** Rubidium (Rb) is an alkali metal which is lower in the periodic table than potassium. It reacts with chlorine.

a) Write a balanced equation for the reaction.

....

(3 marks)

b) Explain why rubidium is stored in oil.

....

....

(2 marks)

c) Explain, in terms of electrons, why rubidium is more reactive than potassium.

EXAM ALERT

> Students have struggled with exam questions similar to this in the past – **be prepared!** ResultsPlus

> Remember to talk about 'more electron shells' and that the outer electron shell is further from the nucleus for the elements at the bottom of the group.

....

....

....

....

(4 marks)

Halogens

D-C   1   The table shows the electronic configurations of some atoms. Put a tick in the boxes to show any atoms that are halogens.

> Guided

(2 marks)

Electronic configuration	Halogen
1	
2.7	✓
2.8	
2.8.1	
2.8.7	
2.8.8	

(2 marks)

D-C   2   Sodium (Na) reacts with chlorine (Cl_2) to produce sodium chloride (NaCl).

Write the balanced equation for this reaction. Give the state symbols.

....

....

(2 marks)

D-C   3   State the trend in reactivity of the halogens.

....

....

(1 mark)

B-A*   4   Tin reacts with fluorine to form solid tin fluoride (SnF_4). Iron reacts with chlorine to produce solid iron (III) chloride ($FeCl_3$). Write the balanced equation for these reactions. Give the state symbols.

   a)   tin: ....

(3 marks)

   b)   iron (III): ....

(3 marks)

B-A*   5   The element astatine (At) is a halogen. It is lower in group 7 than iodine.

   a)   Suggest the state of astatine at room temperature. Explain how you worked out your answer.

....

....

(2 marks)

   b)   An aluminium ion has a charge 3+. Suggest the formula for aluminium astatide.

....

(1 mark)

Had a go ☐ Nearly there ☐ Nailed it! ☐

More halogen reactions

D-C

1 Write the balanced equation for the production of hydrogen bromide (HBr) from hydrogen and bromine.

> **Guided**

$H_2 + Br_2 \rightarrow$ ....

(3 marks)

D-C

2 a) When chlorine is added to a colourless solution of sodium iodide, the solution turns brown.

> Iodine forms a brown solution although it is a grey solid and a purple gas.

   i) Explain what is happening in the reaction.

   ....

   ....

   (2 marks)

   ii) Complete the word equation for the reaction.

   .... $\rightarrow$ sodium chloride + ...

   (1 mark)

b) When chlorine is added to sodium fluoride, no reaction is observed. Explain what this tells you about the reactivity of chlorine and fluorine.

   ....

   ....

   (2 marks)

B-A*

3 You are provided with some chlorine water, bromine water, sodium iodide solution and sodium bromide solution (colourless). Describe how you could use these chemicals to show the position of bromine in the order of reactivity of the halogens.

   ....

   ....

   ....

   ....

   (4 marks)

B-A*

4 a) Gas X is a halogen. When the gas is bubbled through a colourless solution of sodium bromide the solution turns orange/brown. State what the gas X could be.

   ....

   (1 mark)

b) Write a balanced equation for the reaction.

   ....

   ....

   (2 marks)

Noble gases

D-C
Guided

1 The density of hydrogen is 0.09 g/cm³ and the density of helium is 0.18 g/cm³. A balloon full of hydrogen will lift a greater weight than the same balloon full of helium.

Explain why helium is preferred to hydrogen for use in large airships used to carry people.

Helium is ....

so there is no risk of ....

(2 marks)

D-C

2 The table gives data about the noble gases.

> Temperatures with less negative numbers are higher temperatures so −8°C is warmer than −10°C.

Element	Melting point (°C)	Boiling point (°C)	Density (g/cm³)
helium	−272	−269	0.18
neon	−248	−246	0.90
argon	−189	−186	1.78
krypton	−157	−152	3.74
xenon	−111	−108	5.86
radon	−71	−62	9.73

a) Which noble gas has the highest boiling point?

....

(1 mark)

b) Which of the noble gases has a higher melting point than argon and a lower density than xenon? Put a cross (☒) in the box next to your answer.

☐ **A** helium   ☐ **B** neon   ☐ **C** krypton   ☐ **D** radon

c) A student made two statements about the noble gases.
  1 They are liquid over only a small range of temperatures.
  2 Their boiling points are proportional to their density.

Use the data in the table to decide which of these statements are correct. Put a cross (☒) in the box next to your answer.

☐ **A** 1 only   ☐ **B** 2 only   ☐ **C** both 1 and 2   ☐ **D** neither

(1 mark)

B-A

3 Explain, in terms of electron configurations, why the noble gases are unreactive.

....
....
....

(2 marks)

B-A*

4 Nitrogen is not a noble gas but played a part in the discovery of argon, which is a noble gas. Explain how experiments with nitrogen helped chemists discover argon.

....
....
....
....

(4 marks)

Had a go ☐ **Nearly there** ☐ **Nailed it!** ☐

Chemistry extended writing 2

The alkali metals are found in group 1 of the periodic table. They get their name because they form an alkaline solution when they react with water.

There are six members of the group of alkali metals.

Describe how the alkali metals react with water and explain why the elements in the group have different reactivities.

(6 marks)

You will be more successful in extended writing questions if you plan your answer before you start writing.

This question is really asking a series of related questions. These are:

- What do you see when the alkali metals react with water? (Not all the alkali metals behave the same, so pick the one you know the most about – this will probably be sodium or potassium. As the question says, the reaction is similar for all the members of the group.)

- How does the reactivity vary? (Remember that reactivity changes in the group, so there is no need to write about each member individually – just describe how the reactivity changes as you go up or down the group).

- Why does this change in reactivity take place?

Try to include appropriate technical terms when you can.

Be particularly careful when you talk about the process of the metal reacting – you need to use words like atom, electron and ion very carefully here.

Chemists often use equations to describe what is happening in a chemical reaction. You might find it useful to include an equation as part of your description.

....

....

....

....

....

....

....

....

....

....

....

....

....

....

Chemistry extended writing 3

As well as being used by forensic scientists, chromatography is also used by food scientists to identify the substances used as colourings in foods. This is important to make sure that the colourings are permitted for use in food for people.

The diagram shows the results of a chromatography experiment on a new food colouring, which may be a mixture of different substances. Four reference food colours, E101, E110, E120 and E163, have also been shown.

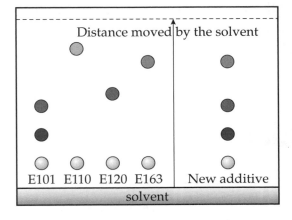

Describe how the food scientist will use chromatography to identify which substances the new additive contains.

(6 marks)

You will be more successful with extended writing questions if you plan your answer before you start writing.

Look at the question and at the information in the diagram before starting to write your answer. You should say something about what has happened in the chromatography experiment and how the process is going to be used. Then you can start analysing the information given in the diagram. Can you 'match the dots' to help identify the substances present in the new additive?

Remember that, at the end of your answer, you should give a summary of the analysis that you have done. This can be a simple statement of what substances you think are present in the new additive.

....

....

....

....

....

....

....

....

....

....

....

....

....

....

....

Had a go ☐   Nearly there ☐   Nailed it! ☐

Temperature changes

D-C

Guided

1 When copper carbonate is heated, carbon dioxide is given off and copper oxide is formed. Explain why this is an endothermic reaction.

More heat energy is needed to .... in copper carbonate than is

.... in the products. So heat is ....

(3 marks)

D-C

2 Sodium reacts with oxygen to produce sodium oxide. Explain why this is an exothermic reaction.

....

....

....

(3 marks)

B-A

3 During the electrolysis of water, the water decomposes into hydrogen and oxygen. This is shown in the diagram.

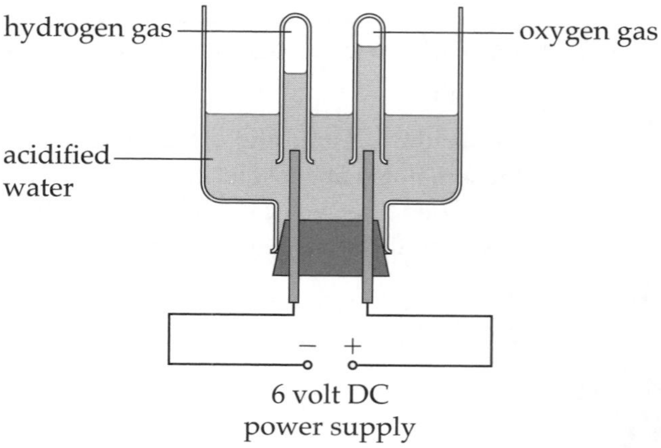

hydrogen gas ——————⌐ ⌐—————— oxygen gas

acidified —— water

a) Suggest why electrolysis is considered an endothermic reaction.

....

....

....

....

(2 marks)

− +

6 volt DC power supply

b) Write the balanced equation for the decomposition of water into hydrogen and oxygen.

....

....

(3 marks)

B-A

4 The diagram is a simple graphical representation of the energy changes occurring when methane and oxygen produce carbon dioxide and water.

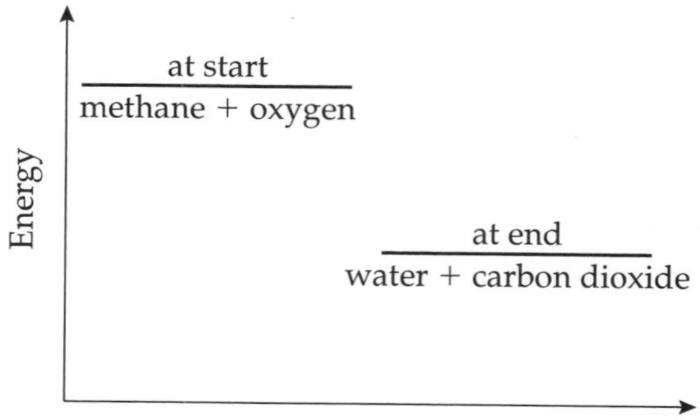

Explain what this diagram tells you about the energy changes taking place in this reaction.

....

....

....

....

....

....

at start
_____
methane + oxygen

at end
_____
water + carbon dioxide

Energy

(3 marks)

Rates of reaction 1

D-C

EXAM ALERT

1 The graph shows how the volume of gas produced changes with time when excess marble chips are added to 200 cm^3 of acid.

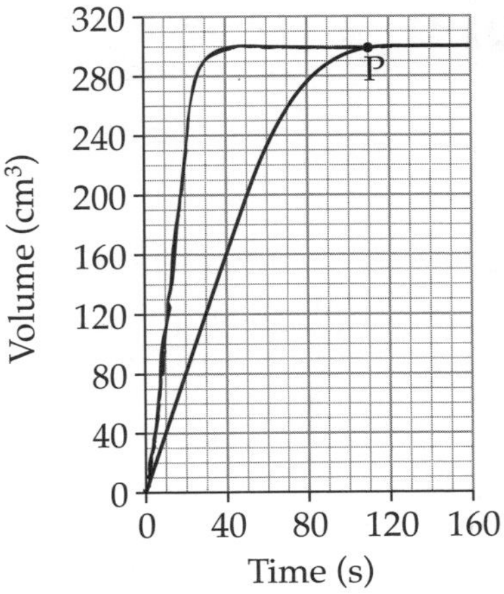

> Students have struggled with exam questions similar to this in the past – **be prepared!**
>
> ResultsPlus

> Sometimes you might be asked about practical work you have done at school – it is a good idea to revise your practical work.

a) How much gas was produced in this reaction?   Volume .... cm^3

(1 mark)

b) Suggest how long it took for the reaction to finish: ....

(1 mark)

c) Describe how the rate of the reaction changes with time in the section from the start to point P.

....

....

(2 marks)

Guided

d) The reaction was repeated at a higher temperature. All the other variables were kept the same. Draw a line on the same set of axes to show how the volume of gas produced changes with time. Label this line T.

(2 marks)

e) The reaction was repeated at the original temperature, with 200 cm^3 of acid which was more dilute. Draw a line on the same set of axes to show how the volume of gas produced changes with time. Label this line D.   **(2 marks)**

B-A*

2 Look at the graph above. Explain why the rate of reaction at P is changing as it does.

....

....

....

....

(4 marks)

Rates of reaction 2

D-C 1 The graph shows the results of an investigation into the effect of size of marble chips on the rate of reaction with 50 cm³ of dilute hydrochloric acid.

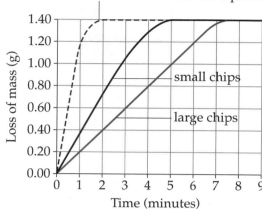

what the curve might look like if the marble was crushed into a powder

a) State the reason for the loss of mass.

....

(1 mark)

b) Explain how decreasing the size of the marble chips (but keeping all other variables the same) would affect the rate of reaction.

....

....

(2 marks)

> You can estimate better if you use a ruler or paper edge to draw a vertical line at an appropriate place. Then draw a horizontal line where the vertical meets the graph.

Guided c) Estimate the average rate of loss of mass in the first 4 minutes of the reaction, when using small chips. Show your working.

loss of mass at 4 mins = ... g

rate of loss = loss/time = ...

Rate .... g/min

(3 marks)

D-C 2 a) Inside a catalytic converter there is a honeycomb-shaped structure. This structure has a thin layer of the catalyst on its surface. Explain why the catalyst is made in this way.

....

....

(2 marks)

b) Explain why catalytic converters work better if the engine has been running for some time.

....

....

....

(3 marks)

Relative masses and formulae

> You will need the following relative atomic masses to answer the questions on this page:
> hydrogen = 1, carbon = 12, oxygen = 16, magnesium = 24, potassium = 39.
>
> An empirical formula is the simplest ratio of the atoms in a substance. The actual number of atoms in a molecule might be different.

> You need to understand how to carry out these calculations – make sure that you practise your method.

1 The diagram shows apparatus set up to find the empirical formula for magnesium oxide. The heated magnesium combines with oxygen in the air.

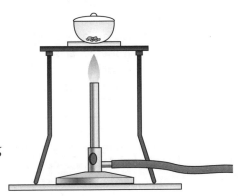

Here is a set of results for this experiment:

　mass of empty crucible = 20.74 g

　mass of container + magnesium = 20.99 g

　mass of container after reaction has finished = 21.15 g

Find the empirical formula for magnesium oxide.

mass of magnesium used = 20.99 − 20.74 g = ... g

mass of oxygen reacted = 21.15 − 20.99 = ... g

Mg = 0.25 / 24 = 0.0104　　| Divide the mass of the magnesium by its relative atomic mass. |

O = ... / 16　= ....　| Do the same for the oxygen – divide the mass of the oxygen by its relative atomic mass. |

Mg = 0.0104 / .... = ...　O = ... / .... = ...　| Then divide both numbers by the smallest number to find the ratio. |

Empirical formula is ....

(3 marks)

2 Find the empirical formula for:

a) an oxide of carbon that contains 1.2 g of carbon and 3.2 g of oxygen.

Empirical formula of this oxide is ....

(3 marks)

b) a sample of potassium oxide that contains 15.6 g of potassium and 3.2 g of oxygen.

Empirical formula of potassium oxide is ....

(3 marks)

Had a go ☐ Nearly there ☐ Nailed it! ☐

Empirical formulae

You will need the following relative atomic masses to answer the questions on this page:
hydrogen = 1, carbon = 12, nitrogen = 14, oxygen = 16, sulfur = 32.

1 The diagram shows a methane molecule.

Calculate the percentage composition by mass of hydrogen in methane.

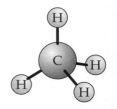

There are four atoms of hydrogen in each methane molecule. Calculate the relative formula mass by adding together all the relative atomic masses of the atoms in the molecule.

The relative formula mass of methane

$$= (4 \times 1) + (1 \times 12)$$

$$=$$

Calculate the percentage of hydrogen by mass by dividing the relative atomic mass of hydrogen in the molecule by the formula mass of the whole molecule and then multiplying by 100.

Percentage of hydrogen by mass $= \dfrac{(4 \times 1)}{16} \times 100$

$$=$$

Percentage composition by mass ....%

(3 marks)

2 Calculate the percentage composition by mass of carbon in carbon dioxide, CO_2.

Percentage composition by mass ....%

(3 marks)

3 Calculate the percentage composition by mass of nitrogen in nitric acid, HNO_3.

Percentage composition by mass ....%

(3 marks)

4 Three fertilisers that contain nitrogen are ammonium sulfate, $(NH_4)_2SO_4$, ammonium nitrate, NH_4NO_3 and urea, $CO(NH_2)_2$. By calculation, show which of these contains the highest percentage of nitrogen by mass.

The highest percentage composition by mass is for ....

(4 marks)

Masses of reactants and products

> You will need the following relative atomic masses to answer the questions on this page:
> hydrogen = 1, lithium = 7, oxygen = 16, aluminium = 27, iron = 56.

 1 A mass of 0.36 g of water was separated into hydrogen and oxygen by electrolysis.

$$2H_2O \rightarrow 2H_2 + O_2$$

Guided

Calculate how much oxygen was produced.

relative formula mass of water = 2 × (2 × 1 + 16) = ...

relative formula mass of oxygen = 2 × .... = ...

.... g of water produces .... g of oxygen

1 g water produces $\frac{..........}{36}$ g oxygen

0.36 g water produces .... g oxygen

mass of oxygen produced .... g

(3 marks)

EXAM ALERT

Students have struggled with exam questions similar to this in the past – **be prepared!** **ResultsPlus**	Always show your working, so even if you make a mistake you may still get some marks. Ask your teacher for help if you don't understand how to do these calculations.

 2 Lithium (Li) reacts with oxygen to produce lithium oxide.

$$4Li + O_2 \rightarrow 2Li_2O$$

Calculate the mass of oxygen that reacts with 5.6 g of lithium.

mass of oxygen .... g

(2 marks)

 3 Aluminium (Al) reacts with iron oxide to produce aluminium oxide and iron.

$$2Al + Fe_2O_3 \rightarrow Al_2O_3 + 2Fe$$

a) Calculate the mass of aluminium needed to produce 672 g of iron.

mass of aluminium .... g

(2 marks)

b) Calculate the mass of iron oxide needed to produce 224 g of iron in this reaction.

mass of iron oxide .... g

(2 marks)

Yields

You will need the following relative atomic masses to answer the questions on this page:
hydrogen = 1, oxygen = 16.

 1 Calculate the percentage yield from a reaction which has an actual yield of 30 g instead of the theoretical yield of 40 g.

$$\text{percentage yield} = \frac{\text{actual yield}}{\text{theoretical yield}} \times 100\%$$

$$= \text{.........} \times 100\%$$

percentage yield .... %
(2 marks)

 2 The graph shows how the mass of gas produced in a reaction changes with time.

    a) State the yield of this reaction in 4 s.

....

(1 mark)

    b) If the theoretical yield after 4 s is 0.09 kg, calculate the percentage yield.

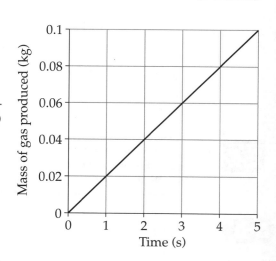

percentage yield .... %
(2 marks)

 3 A chemist calculates that 200 cm³ of hydrochloric acid will react with 100 cm³ of sodium hydroxide to produce 5 g of sodium chloride. She measures exactly 200 cm³ of the acid in a measuring cylinder. She then pours this acid into a flask containing the sodium hydroxide.

Explain why she is likely to produce less than 5 g of sodium chloride.

....

....

(2 marks)

 4 Hydrogen is made when methane reacts with steam according to the equation $CH_4 + H_2O \rightarrow 3H_2 + CO$. In practice, 2.4 kg of methane produced only 0.80 kg of hydrogen.

    a) Calculate the percentage yield.

(3 marks)

    b) Suggest one reason why the percentage yield is less than 100 %.

....

(1 mark)

Waste and profit

C-E   **1**   Burning coal produces solid ash and gases such as carbon dioxide and sulfur dioxide as waste products. Dealing with the waste products from this process is expensive.

Suggest ways that dealing with the waste products will reduce profits.

....

....

(2 marks)

D-C   **2**   State three reasons why people who live in a small town might complain about the siting of a chemical factory near the town.

....

....

....

(3 marks)

B-A*   **3**   Here are three reactions:

Guided

1: iron oxide (Fe_2O_3) plus carbon monoxide (CO) forms iron (Fe) plus carbon dioxide (CO_2)

2: iron oxide plus carbon forms iron plus carbon dioxide

3: nitrogen (N_2) plus hydrogen (H_2) forms ammonia (NH_3)

a) Write balanced equations for these reactions.

Fe_2O_3 + ... CO ....

(2 marks)

$2Fe_2O_3$ + ... C ....

(2 marks)

N_2 + ...

(2 marks)

b) Suggest why carbon dioxide in reaction 1 and reaction 2 is regarded as an unwanted product.

....

(1 mark)

c) High temperatures are used when ammonia is produced on a large scale. Although this makes the reaction faster, it decreases the yield. Suggest how this use of high temperatures may affect the profit made by the chemical company.

....

....

(2 marks)

Had a go ☐ Nearly there ☐ Nailed it! ☐

Chemistry extended writing 4

Endothermic reactions are less common than exothermic reactions. One common endothermic reaction is dissolving ammonium chloride in water.

Describe how the temperature change for this reaction can be investigated in the laboratory. Your description should make it clear how you will collect good quality evidence.

(6 marks)

You will be more successful in extended writing questions if you plan your answer before you start writing.

Your description of the experiment needs to include:

- the apparatus you would use
- the substances you would use
- the measurements that you would make.

Part of the question asks you to consider the quality of the evidence that you collect. This involves:

- using the correct equipment to make the measurements as well as you can
- making sure that you collect enough results to be confident that your answer is correct.

....

....

....

....

....

....

....

....

....

....

....

....

....

....

....

....

....

....

....

....

Chemistry extended writing 5

Many factors affect the rate of chemical reactions. For example, the reaction between hydrochloric acid and calcium carbonate is faster if the calcium carbonate is powdered than if it is in the form of marble chips.

Explain the effect that changes in concentration and temperature have on the rate on a chemical reaction, such as that between hydrochloric acid and calcium carbonate.

(6 marks)

You will be more successful in extended writing questions if you plan your answer before you start writing.

This question has been asked in the context of the reaction of hydrochloric acid with calcium carbonate. This is a familiar reaction – but if you haven't seen it, don't worry – the question can be answered generally about any chemical reaction.

Note that the question asks about only two factors influencing the rate of reaction: concentration and temperature. Do not waste time by writing about any other factors that influence the rate of a reaction.

Remember that an 'explain' question wants you to say *what* happens and *why* it happens. So, you should:

- State what happens to the rate in a reaction when these factors are changed (it is probably easier to describe what happens when they are increased).
- Explain why these changes occur. Here you will need to use your knowledge of the 'collision theory'.
- Take care with the words you use. Chemists need to be precise about the use of 'atom', 'ion' and 'molecule'. Here, when you are talking about the substances reacting, it is probably better to refer to 'particles' of the reacting chemicals.

Remember that a good answer will include precise use of detailed scientific terminology, including the idea of particles, collisions and the minimum energy needed for the reaction to occur.

....
....
....
....
....
....
....
....
....
....
....
....
....
....
....
....

Static electricity

 1 Complete the table below showing the properties of the particles that make up atoms.

Property	Particle		
	Proton	**Neutron**	**Electron**
relative charge		0 (neutral)	
relative mass			negligible
position in atom	in nucleus		

(3 marks)

 2

Guided

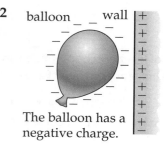

balloon __ __ wall

The balloon has a negative charge.

A student gives a rubber balloon a negative charge by rubbing it on his jumper and then holds it near a wall. Explain why the balloon sticks to the wall.

> Try to use the words 'induction' or 'induced' in your answer.

The negative charges on the balloon repel .... charges in the wall producing an

.... charge on the surface of the wall that .... the balloon.

(3 marks)

B-A* **3** A student rubs a polythene rod with a cloth.

a) The student observes that the cloth is attracted to the rod. Explain why this happens.

....

....

(2 marks)

EXAM ALERT

b) The student rubs another rod. Describe how the student could show that the two rods have been given the same charge.

> Students have struggled with exam questions similar to this in the past – **be prepared!** ResultsPlus

> Remember which particles in the atom can move.

....

....

....

....

(2 marks)

Uses and dangers

D-C
Guided

1　In a murder mystery the victim is in a carpeted room filled with an odourless, flammable gas. He walks to the door, grasps the metal handle and the gas explodes.

Explain how the murderer arranged the death of the victim in the gas explosion.

When the victim walked over the carpet he became charged.

....

....

(3 marks)

B-C

2　Aircraft become charged by friction with air.

a)　State a reason why this could be dangerous when the aircraft is being refuelled.

....

....

(1 mark)

b)　Explain how the aircraft is refuelled safely.　　　| State what is done and why it works. |

....

....

(2 marks)

B-C

3　Static electricity is used in the spray painting of car bodies and bicycle frames.

a)　Give a reason why the paint and the object being sprayed are given opposite charges.

....

(1 mark)

b)　State two advantages of using static electricity for spray painting.

....

....

(2 marks)

B-A*

4　Many tall buildings have a lightning rod made of a thick strip of metal. When a charged rain cloud is nearby, lightning is more likely to strike the rod than unprotected buildings or people.

Explain what happens to the lightning rod in an electrical storm where the cloud is negatively charged.

| Think about why the lightning should strike the rod and not another part of the tall building. |

....

....

....

....

(4 marks)

Electric currents

You will find this equation useful: charge = current × time $Q = I \times t$

D-C **1** The electric current flowing in a circuit is 4 amperes.

   a) Explain what is meant by an electric current.

   ....

   ....

   (2 marks)

Guided **b)** The current flows for 8 seconds. How much charge has flowed? Give the unit.

> You will be given this equation at the beginning of the exam paper but you should remember the units for charge, current and time.

   Current = 4 amperes, time = 8 s

   So charge = ... × ....

   Charge .... unit ....

   (3 marks)

B-C **2** A cell in an electric circuit causes charged particles to move along the wires.

   cell

   a) Name the particle that carries the charge.

   ....

   (1 mark)

   b) Describe the current supplied by the cell.

   ....

   ....

   (2 marks)

B-A*

EXAM ALERT

   c) The cell provides 15 coulombs of charge in 20 s. Calculate the current flowing in the circuit. State the unit.

> Students have struggled with exam questions similar to this in the past – **be prepared!**
>
> ResultsPlus

> Always show your working. If you get the final answer wrong you may still get some marks if you have done some of the working correctly.

   Current .... unit ....

   (4 marks)

B-A* **3** A charged rod has a charge of 60 C. When it discharges to earth there is a current of 20 A. Calculate the time it takes for the rod to become completely discharged.

   Time .... s

   (3 marks)

Current and voltage

D-C 1 Look at the circuit shown in the diagram below.

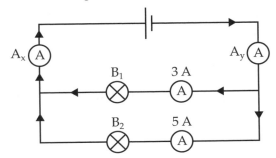

a) What is the reading on ammeter A_x?

....

(1 mark)

> Remember that the currents through the two bulbs join up to pass through the ammeter.

b) State how you could increase the size of the current flowing through the circuit.

....

(1 mark)

> Guided

c) Explain why the current measured by ammeter A_y is the same as ammeter A_x.

The electrons move around the ....

so the current leaving the cell is the same as the .... returning to it.

(2 marks)

B-A* 2 A student is investigating the energy transferred by a lamp in a circuit.

a) Draw a circuit below to show how she could measure the potential difference across a lamp supplied by a battery.

(2 marks)

b) The student records a potential difference of 3 V across the lamp. Calculate the energy transferred to the lamp when 10 C of charge pass through the lamp. State the unit.

> You will need to remember the definition of potential difference in terms of energy transferred to a unit charge.

Energy transferred .... unit ....

(4 marks)

Resistance, current and voltage

You will need the following equation: potential difference = current × resistance $V = I \times R$

> In an exam this equation will be printed at the start of the paper.

 1 Look at the diagram below

> **Guided**

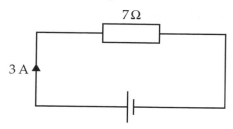

Calculate the potential difference supplied to the circuit. State the unit.

Current =

Resistance =

Potential difference =

Potential difference .... unit ....

(3 marks)

 2 The cell in the circuit diagram in question 1 is changed for a power pack with a variable potential difference.

a) Draw a line on the graph to show how the current through the fixed resistor changes as the potential difference supplied to the circuit is changed. Mark this line A.

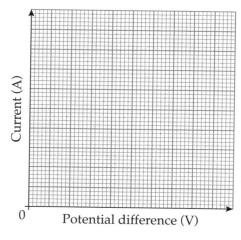

> In the equation $V = I \times R$, think about what happens to I when V increases and R is fixed.

(2 marks)

b) Explain how the line would be different if the fixed resistor were replaced by one with a larger resistance.

....

....

(2 marks)

 3 A student set up a circuit containing a resistor. He measured the current through the resistor as 1.6 A and the potential difference across it as 2.4 V. Calculate the resistance. State the unit.

Resistance .... unit ....

(4 marks)

Changing resistances

 1 Look at the graphs shown below.

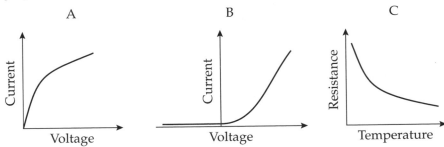

a) Which graph shows the characteristics of a diode? .... **(1 mark)**

b) Describe what happens to the current through the component shown in graph A as the voltage increases.

....

....

(2 marks)

c) Describe what happens to the current through the component shown in graph C as the temperature rises when there is a fixed voltage across it.

....

....

(2 marks)

> Remember the equation $V = I \times R$. If V is constant then I must increase as R decreases.

 2 An electric circuit in a car has a lamp connected in series with the battery and a thermistor.

> Guided

The lamp will only light up when the current is above a certain value. Explain the condition necessary for the lamp to light up.

The lamp lights up when the temperature is .... because the current through the

lamp and the thermistor will ....

....

(2 marks)

 3 The diagram shows a circuit in which a light-dependent resistor makes a night-light turn off in the daytime.
Explain how the circuit works.

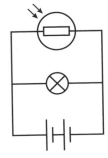

....

....

(2 marks)

Transferring energy

You may find the following equations useful in these questions.

Electrical power = current × potential difference $P = I \times V$

Energy transferred = current × potential difference × time $E = I \times V \times t$

D-B

Guided

1   A student plugs her mobile phone into a charger and switches it on at the mains socket. She is surprised to find the charger getting warm. Explain why the charger gets warm.

When the charger is plugged in a current flows. The energy is ....

....

(2 marks)

D-B

2   a)   A hotplate is used to heat up a saucepan of water. The hotplate uses the mains voltage of 230 V. The electric current through the hotplate is 5 A. Calculate the power of the hotplate in watts (W).

> Read the question carefully to find out which quantity you are asked to calculate and what information you are given, and then choose the equation you need.

Power .... W

(2 marks)

b)   A mobile phone has a battery that produces a potential difference of 4 V. When making a call it uses a current of 0.2 A. A student makes a call lasting 30 seconds.

Calculate the energy transferred by the phone while making the call. State the unit.

Energy transferred .... unit ....

(3 marks)

B-A*

3   The potential difference across a cell is 6 V. The cell delivers 3 W of electrical power to a filament lamp.

a)   Calculate the current flowing through the lamp.

> You will have to rearrange one of the equations given at the top of the page.

Current .... A

(3 marks)

b)   Explain how the electrical energy is transferred to heat in the filament of the lamp.

....

....

(2 marks)

Physics extended writing 1

The resistor in an electric heater connected to the mains voltage (230 V) has a resistance of 53 Ω. Explain why this heater releases about 1 kJ of heat every second when connected to the mains voltage.

(6 marks)

You will be more successful in extended writing questions if you plan your answer before you start writing. In this question, you need to think about the energy transfers that take place when a current flows in a wire.

Some questions to think about are:

- What does the term voltage (or potential difference) mean?
- What is the current flowing through the heater?
- How can the energy transferred be calculated?
- What happens when a current flows through a resistor?

Remember that in an 'explain' question you are expected to say what happens *and why*. Try to use detailed scientific terminology in your answer.

....

....

....

....

....

....

....

....

....

....

....

....

....

....

....

....

....

....

....

....

Vectors and velocity

You may find this formula useful: speed = $\dfrac{\text{distance}}{\text{time}}$

D-C 1 The distance–time graph shows a
student's journey from home to
the shops.

a) Write down the letter that
corresponds to the part of the
student's journey where he:

  i) stands still ....

  ii) runs instead of walks ....

(2 marks)

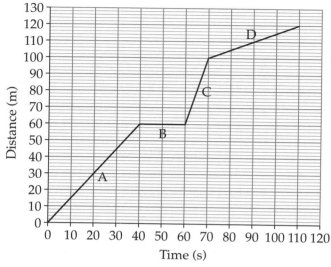

> **Guided** b) Calculate the student's speed in part A of his journey.

In part A, he travels a distance of .... m in a time of .... s

Speed = distance .... (m) / time .... (s)

Speed .... m/s
(2 marks)

c) When the student gets to the shops his displacement from home is less than the distance
he has travelled. Explain this difference.

....

....
(2 marks)

D-C 2 The lift inside the tower of a wind turbine tower takes
24 s to go from the ground to the generator 84 m above.

a) Calculate the speed of the lift. State the unit.

> Recall the difference between
> speed and velocity.

Speed .... unit ....
(3 marks)

b) State the velocity of the lift.

....
(1 mark)

C-A* 3 An athlete runs at a constant speed of 5 m/s around a running track. A complete lap is 400 m.
Calculate the time it took the athlete to complete 1 lap.

Time .... s
(3 marks)

Velocity and acceleration

You will need this equation: acceleration $= \dfrac{\text{change of velocity}}{\text{time taken}}$ $a = \dfrac{(v - u)}{t}$

 1 A sprinter takes 2 s from the start of a race to reach his maximum velocity of 12 m/s in a straight line.

a) Calculate the sprinter's acceleration.

Acceleration .... unit ....

(3 marks)

b) An athlete runs at a constant speed for one whole lap of a circular running track. Explain why she is accelerating.

....

....

(2 marks)

 2 The velocity–time graph shows how the velocity of a car changes with time.

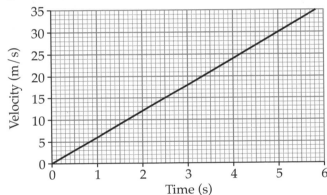

Mark a triangle on the graph to show the velocity increase and the time taken.

a) Calculate the acceleration of the car.

Change in velocity = ... m/s. Time taken for the change = ... s

Acceleration $= \dfrac{\text{change in velocity}}{\text{time taken}} =$

Acceleration .... m/s²

(2 marks)

b) Use the graph to calculate the distance travelled by the car in the first 5 s.

Distance travelled is the area under the line. In this case, it is the area of the triangle made by the line and the time axis up to 5 s.

Distance .... m

(2 marks)

 3 A rocket launches with an acceleration of 20 m/s². Calculate its velocity after 4 s.

Velocity .... m/s

(3 marks)

Resultant forces

D-B 1 A submarine is travelling at a steady depth in the sea. It starts to accelerate. Draw a free body force diagram for all the forces acting on the submarine. Label the forces.

> The lengths of the arrows on a free body force diagram suggest the relative size of forces.

(2 marks)

D-B 2 A cyclist is sitting on his bike waiting for the start of a race.

> Guided

a) Describe the action and reaction forces acting on the cyclist and the bicycle.

The action is the .... and the reaction is

the ....

(2 marks)

b) The race begins and the cyclist pushes on the pedals producing a forward thrust on the bicycle of 30 N. There is resistance from the air of 10 N and friction on the wheels of 6 N. Calculate the resultant force.

> Add up all the forces acting in a straight line. Give forces that act opposite to the thrust a minus sign.

Force .... N

(2 marks)

c) During the race, the resistive forces become equal to the forward thrust. Explain what happens to the velocity of the cyclist.

....

....

(2 marks)

d) At the end of the race the cyclist stops pedalling. Explain what happens next.

....

....

(2 marks)

B-A* 3 A space probe falls towards the Moon. In the Moon's gravitational field the probe has a weight of 1700 N. The probe fires rockets giving an upwards thrust of 1900 N.

a) Calculate the resultant force on the space probe.

Resultant force .... N

(2 marks)

b) Explain the changes in the probe's velocity.

....

....

(2 marks)

Forces and acceleration

You will need this equation: force = mass × acceleration $F = m \times a$

D-C

Guided

1   In an experiment a student pulls a force meter attached to a trolley along a bench. The trolley has frictionless wheels. The force meter gives a reading of 5 N.

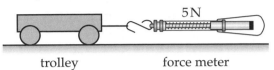

trolley   force meter

In reality there are always friction forces acting, but in this question they can be ignored because it says the trolley has frictionless wheels.

a) Describe what will happen to the trolley.

The trolley will ....

in the direction ....

(2 marks)

b) The student stacks some masses on the trolley and again pulls it with a force of 5 N. Explain why the trolley takes longer to travel the length of the bench.

The acceleration is .... because ....

(2 marks)

D-C

2   When the Soyuz spacecraft returns to Earth from space it is slowed by friction with the air. The spacecraft has a mass of 3000 kg and the craft slows with an average acceleration of $-13 \, m/s^2$.

a) Calculate the average resultant force acting on the spacecraft. State the unit.

Force .... unit ....

(3 marks)

b) State the direction in which the force acts.

....

(1 mark)

B-A*

3   A Formula 1 racing car has a mass of 640 kg. A resultant force of 10 500 N acts on the car.

a) Calculate the acceleration on the racing car. State the unit.

You will have to rearrange the equation given above.

Acceleration .... unit ....

(4 marks)

b) Explain what will happen to the acceleration of the car as its fuel tank empties, assuming the resultant force remains constant.

....

....

(2 marks)

Had a go ☐   Nearly there ☐   Nailed it! ☐

Terminal velocity

You will need the equation: weight = mass × gravitational field strength $W = m \times g$

D-C 1 A bag of potatoes has a mass of 2.5 kg.

> The equation will be given at the start of the exam paper but the question will always tell you the gravitational field strength.

  a) Calculate the weight of the bag of potatoes on Earth. (The Earth's gravitational field strength = 10 N/kg.)

  Weight .... N

  (2 marks)

  b) Explain why the same bag of potatoes would have a smaller weight on the Moon.

> Remember that that the Moon is a lot smaller than the Earth.

  ....

  ....

  (2 marks)

D-C 2 A parachutist has a weight of 900 N including his parachute. He jumps off a high cliff and immediately opens his parachute. His velocity increases at first and then he falls at a constant velocity.

EXAM ALERT

> Students have struggled with exam questions similar to this in the past – **be prepared!** **ResultsPlus**

> Remember that air resistance and weight act throughout the fall through the air.

  a) Which of the following describe the resultant force on the parachutist just before the parachute opens. Put a cross in the box (☒) next to your answer.

  ☐ **A** The resultant force is downwards because there is no air resistance.

  ☐ **B** The resultant force is upwards because there is air resistance.

  ☐ **C** The resultant force is downwards because his weight is greater than air resistance.

  ☐ **D** There is no resultant force because he is falling.   **(1 mark)**

Guided **b)** Just before the parachutist reaches the ground with his parachute open, his acceleration is zero. Explain why the acceleration is zero.

  The air resistance is .... to his weight so the resultant

  force is .... and the acceleration is zero.

  (2 marks)

B-A* 3 In 1971, while standing on the Moon, astronaut David Scott dropped a hammer and a feather simultaneously. The two objects hit the ground together.

  a) Explain what happened in astronaut Scott's demonstration.

  ....

  ....

  (2 marks)

  b) Explain why the demonstration is difficult to do on Earth.

  ....

  ....

  (2 marks)

Stopping distances

40 mph (64 km/h)	12 metres	24 metres
50 mph (80 km/h)	15 metres	38 metres
60 mph (96 km/h)	18 metres	55 metres

thinking distance   braking distance

Speeds may be given in miles per hour (mph) or kilometres per hour (km/h)

D-C 1 A car is travelling at 40 miles per hour.

a) Calculate the stopping distance of the car using the table above. Show your working.

Distance .... metres
(2 marks)

b) The stopping distance of a car can be affected by a number of factors. Explain how the stopping distance of a car is affected if:

Guided
i) the road is wet
The braking distance will be longer because there is reduced ....
....
(3 marks)

ii) the driver is tired
....
....
(3 marks)

D-C 2 Two students investigate how the roughness of a surface affects frictional forces. They measure the force required to pull a block over different surfaces.
State three things the students should do to make the experiment a fair test.
....
....
....
(3 marks)

B-A* 3 The police are investigating an accident involving a car that crashed on a dry, newly surfaced road. The speed limit for this road is 40 miles per hour. The police can tell from tyre marks that the brakes were applied 40 m from where the crash occurred. The car's tyres were in good condition.

Suggest reasons why the car was unable to stop in the space between where the brakes were applied and the site of the crash. Use the chart at the top of this page to help you.
....
....
....
....
(4 marks)

The number of marks available suggest that there are four points to make.

Momentum

You will need the formula: momentum = mass × velocity

D-B   **1**   Calculate the momentum of a car with a mass of 1200 kg driving at 30 m/s from north to south. State the unit.

> **Guided**

Momentum = ... kg × .... m/s

In the .... direction

> The units of momentum are a combination of the units of mass and velocity. Remember that momentum is a vector quantity.

Momentum .... unit ....

(4 marks)

D-B   **2**   Two students are driving 'dodgem' cars at a funfair. The total mass of Student 2 and his car is 200 kg. He is moving at 3 m/s toward the west.

   a)   Calculate the momentum of Student 2 and his car.

Momentum .... kg m/s ....

(2 marks)

   b)   Student 1's car has the same total mass as Student 2's but her car is not moving. Student 2's car collides with Student 1's car.

     i)   Calculate the sum of the momentum of both cars before the collision

Momentum .... kg m/s ....

(1 mark)

     ii)   Explain what happens to the sum of the momentum of both cars after the collision.

....

....

(2 marks)

     iii) Student 2's car stops during the collision. State its momentum after the collision.

....

(1 mark)

     iv) State the momentum of Student 1's car after the collision.

....

(1 mark)

B-A*   **3**   A skater with a mass of 50 kg skates across the ice at 7.2 m/s in a straight line. She collides with her stationary partner who has a mass of 70 kg. They glide off together in the same direction as the first skater was moving. Calculate the velocity with which the pair glide across the ice.

Velocity .... m/s

(3 marks)

Momentum and safety

> Remember that if you take longer to slow down there is less force on you and less chance of damage or injury.

D-C

Guided

1 A person wanted to send a glass ornament to a friend overseas. She decided to wrap the ornament in bubble-wrap before packaging it. On the way to the post office, she dropped the package but the ornament did not break.

a) Explain why dropping an unprotected glass object may break it.

> Think about the mass of the object and what happens to the velocity of the object when it hits the floor.

The falling ornament has ....

The damage is caused on hitting the floor because ....

....

(2 marks)

b) Explain how the bubble-wrap prevented damage to the ornament.

When the package hits the ground the bubble-wrap ....

So reducing ....

(3 marks)

C-B

2 Two students are investigating the time taken to reduce the velocity of a trolley to zero when it hits a barrier. They fit various materials to the front of the trolley that squash or crumple when hit.

> Controlled variables are ones that you need to keep constant throughout an experiment.

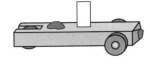

a) State the variables that should be controlled in this experiment.

....

....

(2 marks)

b) Explain why the students are looking for the material that produces the longest stopping time.

....

....

....

(3 marks)

B-A*

3 A front seat passenger wearing a seat belt is in a car involved in a crash. The seatbelt stretches a few centimetres before the passenger stops moving. Explain why seatbelts designed in this way help to reduce injuries.

....

....

(2 marks)

Had a go ☐   Nearly there ☐   Nailed it! ☐

Work and power

You will need the formulae:

work done = force × distance moved in the direction of the force $E = F \times d$

power = $\dfrac{\text{work done}}{\text{time taken}}$ $P = \dfrac{E}{t}$

D–C

> **Guided**

1 Two students pull a wooden block over different surfaces using a force meter. They keep the force constant while pulling the block. They measure the time taken for the pull. Here is one of their results.

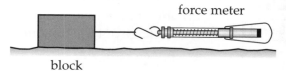

force meter

block

Surface	Distance travelled by block (m)	Force (N)	Time taken (s)
sandpaper	0.6	4	3

a) Calculate the amount of work done on the block in the experiment. State the unit.

> Make sure you choose the correct equation from the ones given at the top of the page.

Work done = Force .... N × Distance .... m

Work done .... unit ....

(3 marks)

b) Calculate the power used to pull the block.

Power = Work done .... J /time taken .... s

Work done .... W

(2 marks)

D–C

2 A racing car has brakes that can transfer 30 000 J of kinetic energy into thermal energy in 2 s. Calculate the braking power of the racing car.

Power .... W

(2 marks)

B–A*

3 A car has an electric motor with a power of 110 kW. The batteries of the car store 55 MJ of energy.

> Remember that 'k' stands for 1000 and 'M' for 1 000 000.

a) Calculate the time the car could run for at full power.

Time .... s

(4 marks)

b) The car is said to have a range of 80 km. Calculate the force applied by the engine assuming that the journey is in a straight line and there is no energy wasted.

Force .... N

(3 marks)

Potential and kinetic energy

You will need these formulae:

gravitational potential energy = mass × gravitational field strength × vertical height
GPE = $m \times g \times h$

kinetic energy = $\frac{1}{2}$ × mass × velocity²   KE = $\frac{1}{2} \times m \times v^2$

 D-C

 Guided

1   A female falcon of mass 1.2 kg is perched on a tower 40 m above the ground.

    a) Calculate the gravitational potential energy of the falcon. The Earth's gravitational field strength is 10 N/kg.

> All the data you need is given in the question or in the introduction to the question.

      GPE = m × g × h

      GPE = ... × .... × h

Gravitational potential energy ....J

(2 marks)

    b) The falcon flies off and then swoops to catch its prey at a speed of 80 m/s. Calculate the kinetic energy of the falcon in flight.

> Be careful with the calculation: velocity² (or v^2) means multiplying the speed by itself.

Kinetic energy ....J

(2 marks)

C-A* 2   In the Middle Ages, battering rams were used to smash down doors of castles. The battering ram was made up of a log weighing 2000 kg suspended by ropes. When the log was pulled back, it rose by 0.5 m.

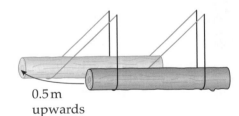

0.5 m
upwards

    a) Calculate the gravitational potential energy gained by the log when it was pulled back.

Gravitational potential energy ....J

(2 marks)

    b) How much work was done in pulling the log back?

Work done ....J

(1 mark)

EXAM ALERT

    c) Calculate the velocity of the battering ram as it reaches the bottom of its swing.

> Students have struggled with exam questions similar to this in the past – **be prepared!** ResultsPlus

> Remember that energy is conserved and work done equals energy transferred.

Velocity .... m/s

(4 marks)

Braking and energy calculations

You will need these formulae:

force = (change in momentum)/time $F = \dfrac{(mv - mu)}{t}$

kinetic energy = $\frac{1}{2}$ × mass × velocity² $KE = \frac{1}{2} \times m \times v^2$

work done = force × distance moved in the direction of the force $E = F \times d$

 1 The NASA missions that delivered the exploration vehicles Spirit and Opportunity to the surface of Mars used airbags for the final stage of the landing. Spirit had a mass of 530 kg and hit the surface with a speed of 25 m/s. The airbags took 0.5 s to compress and stop the craft.

   a) Calculate the change of momentum of the spacecraft as it landed.

Change of momentum .... kg m/s

(2 marks)

   b) Calculate the force acting on the airbags as the spacecraft landed.

Force .... N

(2 marks)

 2 A car of mass 1300 kg travelling at 20 m/s brakes and takes 2.6 s to come to a stop.

 a) Calculate the braking force acting on the car. State the unit.

   v = velocity of the car when it has stopped =

   u = velocity of the car when it starts to brake =

   The braking force = $\dfrac{(mv - mu)}{t}$ =

Force .... unit ....

(3 marks)

   b) Calculate the braking distance of the car.

   The kinetic energy of the car as it starts to brake =

   This amount of work is done to stop the car.

   Distance travelled =

Distance travelled .... m

(6 marks)

 3 A tennis ball with a mass of 0.056 kg, travelling at 50 m/s, hits a tennis racket. The strings of the racket stretch and stop the ball when it has moved a further 0.01 m. Calculate the braking force of the racket on the ball.

> Check which quantities are given in the question and choose the formulae that use those quantities for your calculation.

Force .... N

(5 marks)

Physics extended writing 2

The graph shows how the velocity of two identical cars changes during a straight line race. Both cars only brake when they have passed the finish line.

Analyse the information given in the graph about the motion of the cars during the race.

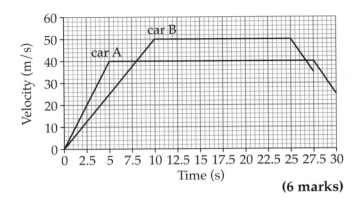

(6 marks)

> You will be more successful in extended writing questions if you plan your answer before you start writing. In this question you need to think about the data provided by the lines for the two cars in the velocity–time graph.
>
> Some questions to think about are:
>
> - Which car had the highest velocity?
> - Which car had the highest acceleration?
> - What distance was the race?
> - How can you tell which car won the race?
> - How does the graph provide this information?

....

....

....

....

....

....

....

....

....

....

....

....

....

....

....

....

....

Physics extended writing 3

Tennis balls and cricket balls can each travel at 100 mph during a game. Cricketers wear protective clothing when facing fast balls but tennis players do not. Being hit by a cricket ball is more painful.

Facts:

- 100 mph is 45 m/s.

- A cricket ball has a mass of 0.15 kg. It will compress by about 0.001 m when hitting a rigid object.

- A tennis ball has a mass of 0.056 kg. It will compress by about 0.02 m when hitting a rigid object.

Compare the forces and work required to stop cricket and tennis balls.

(6 marks)

> You will be more successful in extended writing questions if you plan your answer before you start writing. In this question, you need to think about the energy of both balls in flight and what will happen to them when they are brought to a halt.
>
> Some questions to think about are:
>
> - What is the kinetic energy of each ball?
> - How much work is done in stopping each ball?
> - How much force is needed to stop each ball?

....

....

....

....

....

....

....

....

....

....

....

....

....

....

....

....

Isotopes

D-C

**EXAM
ALERT**

1 Look at the symbol below representing an atom of neon.

$$^{22}_{10}\text{Ne}$$

> Students have struggled with exam questions similar to this in the past – **be prepared!** ResultsPlus

a) State the mass number of this atom.

....

> You need to learn the parts of an atom and how they are represented.

(1 mark)

b) State the number of protons in this atom.

....

(1 mark)

c) Calculate the number of neutrons in this atom.

Number of neutrons ....
(1 mark)

D-C

2 Two atoms each have 17 protons. One atom has 18 neutrons and the other has 20 neutrons.

a) Explain why these atoms are isotopes.

....

....

(2 marks)

Guided

b) The atoms are of the element chlorine. Complete the symbols of the two isotopes.

$$_{17}\text{Cl} \qquad ^{37}\text{Cl}$$

(2 marks)

> You don't have to recall the symbols of elements, but it will help you if you know the symbols for some of the elements that you have learned about in this course.

B-A

3 The symbols of two isotopes of oxygen are shown below.

$$^{16}_{8}\text{O} \qquad ^{18}_{8}\text{O}$$

Compare the structures of the atoms of the two isotopes.

....

....

....

(3 marks)

C-A

4 Write the symbol of a potassium atom (K) that has 19 protons and 20 neutrons in its nucleus.

....

(2 marks)

Ionising radiation

D-C 1

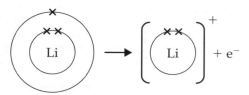

Note that the lithium atom itself is not radioactive.

a) The diagram shows what might happen if a lithium atom was hit by ionising radiation. Explain what the diagram shows.

....

....

(2 marks)

b) If the lithium atom is hit by a beta particle it may become negatively charged. Explain how this could happen.

....

....

(2 marks)

c) A sample of gas is irradiated by radiation from different sources. A detector records the ionisation produced by each source. Three sources were tested: an alpha particle source, a beta particle source and a gamma ray source.

The bar chart shows the counts recorded for each source tested in turn.

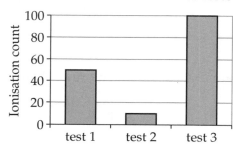

The higher the bar, the more atoms in the gas that have been ionised.

State which test is for:

i) alpha ....   ii) beta ....   iii) gamma ....   **(2 marks)**

B-A* 2 A student suggests that the penetrating powers of alpha and gamma radiation are related to their structure. Use your knowledge of alpha and gamma radiation to evaluate the student's suggestion.

> **Guided**

Alpha radiation is more .... than gamma radiation; alpha radiation

is .... , which get slowed down quite easily. Gamma radiation is

.... , which are harder to stop.

(3 marks)

B-A* 3 Explain why a sample of a radioactive substance constantly gives out ionising radiation, but it is not possible to predict when an individual atom will decay.

....

....

(2 marks)

Nuclear reactions

D-C 1   Which of the following is **not** an example of a nuclear reaction? Put a cross in the box (☒) next to your answer.

☐ **A** an atom emitting an alpha particle

☐ **B** two hydrogen atoms fusing to form a helium atom

☐ **C** a beta particle knocking an electron from an atom

☐ **D** a uranium atom splitting into two smaller atoms and releasing neutrons   **(1 mark)**

D-C 2   The splitting of one uranium atom can set off a chain reaction.

Guided

a) The following sentences give the stages in a chain reaction. Put the letters at the start of each sentence in the order in which the stages take place.

A A neutron hits a uranium-235 nucleus.

B The neutrons released can go on to hit other uranium-235 nuclei.

C More uranium nuclei split producing even more neutrons.

D The uranium-235 nucleus absorbs the neutron and begins to split.

E Two or more neutrons and two daughter nuclei are formed and a lot of energy is released.

A ....   **(2 marks)**

> Read the sentences to yourself in the order that you have put them to check your answer.

b) The process described above is an uncontrolled chain reaction. Explain what is different about the controlled chain reaction used in a nuclear reactor.

....

....

                                                                            (2 marks)

c) Explain the meaning of the term 'daughter nuclei'.

....

....

                                                                            (2 marks)

B-A* 3 **a)** Explain why a power station using fossil fuels has to be supplied with fuel almost every day while a nuclear power station needs refuelling less frequently.

> Compare the amounts of fossil and nuclear fuel required to produce the same amount of energy.

....

....

                                                                            (2 marks)

b) Suggest why radioactive materials are often used on spacecraft travelling to the outer solar system.

....

....

                                                                            (2 marks)

Nuclear power

D-C **1** **a)** A nuclear reactor produces waste material. State what the waste material consists of.

....

(1 mark)

b) State the reason why waste material from nuclear power stations is dangerous.

....

(1 mark)

D-B **2** A nuclear reactor contains fuel rods, control rods and a moderator.

> Keep your answers short and to the point, and use scientific terms.

Guided

a) Explain the function of the:

i) fuel rods

They contain the nuclear .... which undergoes ....

(2 marks)

ii) control rods

....

....

(2 marks)

iii) moderator

....

....

(2 marks)

b) State how the amount of energy released by the reactor can be increased.

....

(1 mark)

B-A* **3**

'A nuclear power station is just like any fossil fuel power station except that it uses nuclear fuel.'

Explain why the energy changes in a nuclear power station make this statement only partly true.

> You need to recall the energy changes that take place throughout a power station so you can contrast nuclear and fossil fuels.

....

....

....

(3 marks)

Fusion – our future?

D-C   1   In 1989 Martin Fleischmann and Stanley Pons announced that they had evidence that deuterium and tritium nuclei could fuse at a temperature of 50°C to form helium nuclei. The announcement was made to newspaper reporters, who called the idea 'cold fusion'.

> Remember that a 'theory' is an idea that has been tested and is supported by the evidence.

Guided   a)   Describe how the publicity about cold fusion was different to the normal way that a scientific discovery is announced.

The announcement was made in .... instead of ....

(2 marks)

b)   Explain what is needed to persuade scientists that cold fusion happens.

....

....

(2 marks)

EXAM ALERT   Students have struggled with exam questions similar to this in the past – **be prepared!**   ResultsPlus

> When answering questions on fusion reactions always refer to *nuclei*.

D-B   2   a)   Stars like our Sun are mostly made up of hydrogen. Describe the process that releases energy in stars.

....

....

(2 marks)

b)   People sometimes confuse the process that takes place in stars with what happens in the nuclear power stations that have been in use for the last sixty years. State the differences between what happens in fission and fusion, and the conditions needed for each process.

....

....

(2 marks)

B-A*   3   For fifty years scientists have been trying to start a controlled fusion reaction but have yet to achieve commercial success, while the Sun has been shining for over 4 billion years.

a)   State the conditions in the Sun that allow fusion reactions to occur.

....

....

(2 marks)

b)   Explain why these conditions are needed for fusion reactions to take place.

....

....

(2 marks)

c)   State a reason why we do not use energy from fusion reactors to generate electricity.

> You don't have to go into detail about experimental fusion reactors.

....

(1 mark)

Changing ideas

D-C 1 In the First World War, soldiers and airmen were issued with watches that had figures and hands that glowed in the dark. The luminous paint contained radium, a radioactive element discovered in 1898. The watches still give out a dangerous level of ionising radiation today. In the 1920s, many of the women who painted the watches became seriously ill.

> Think about why scientific ideas change over time.

> **Guided**

a) Explain why the radium paint was used in the watches then even though today it is known to be harmful.

At the time the effects of radium were not known so it was thought that the radium paint

was ....

(2 marks)

b) Explain why radium paint was later banned from being used on watches.

....

....

(2 marks)

D-C 2 Radioactive materials are harmful.
Suggest precautions you would take:

> You should recall the precautions you need to take when handling radioactive materials.

a) to protect yourself if you were working with radioactive materials

....

(1 mark)

b) to lift radioactive material from a container

....

(1 mark)

c) to move radioactive material around the country.

....

(1 mark)

C-A 3 a) Describe the direct harmful effects of a high dose of ionising radiation.

> Ionising radiation can have immediate effects or cause illnesses that appear some time in the future.

....

....

(2 marks)

b) Some scientists think that even the smallest amounts of ionising radiation can cause mutations leading to cancer. Suggest reasons why this might be.

....

....

(2 marks)

Nuclear waste

D-B 1 The nuclear waste from power stations and other uses is put into three groups:

- High level waste (HLW) – produces large amounts of ionising radiation for about 50 years before becoming ILW.
- Intermediate level waste (ILW) – produces a moderate amount of ionising radiation for thousands of years.
- Low level waste (LLW) – remains slightly radioactive for thousands of years.

Guided **a)** Suggest which group the following items of waste are put in:

    i) Waste from hospital radiography departments: LLW

    ii) Clothes of nuclear power station workers: ....

    iii) The products of nuclear reactions: ....

    iv) Containers of nuclear fuels: ....

                                                                  (4 marks)

b) Explain why HLW is sealed inside glass blocks.

....

....

                                                                 (2 marks)

c) HLW and ILW may have to be stored underground for thousands of years. State a precaution that must be taken when choosing a suitable site.

....

                                                                  (1 mark)

d) One idea for disposal is to use rockets to carry nuclear waste into space. Suggest why this idea has not been used.

....

....

                                                                  (2 marks)

B-A* 2 **a)** Supporters of nuclear power give one main advantage of nuclear power over the using fossil fuels relating to climate change. Explain this advantage.

> Compare the products of nuclear and combustion reactions and what advantage this gives to nuclear power.

....

....

                                                                  (2 marks)

b) The problem of disposing of nuclear waste is a serious disadvantage of nuclear power. Suggest other reasons why public opinion has turned against nuclear power in many countries.

....

....

                                                                  (2 marks)

Half-life

1 A sample of thallium-208 contains 16 million atoms. Thalium-208 has a half-life of 3.1 minutes.

a) State the number of nuclei that will have decayed in 3.1 minutes.

....

....

(1 mark)

> Students have struggled with exam questions similar to this in the past – **be prepared!** ResultsPlus

> Remember that half-life is the time for half the nuclei in a sample to decay, not the time for one atom to decay.

b) Calculate the number of unstable thallium nuclei left after 9.3 minutes.

Number of unstable thallium nuclei left ....

(2 marks)

2 A student measured the activity of a radioactive sample for 30 minutes. He plotted the graph of activity against time shown below.

> Guided

Use the graph to calculate the half-life of the sample.

> You could take any point on the line as the starting point for calculating the half-life.

The activity is 400 Bq at .... min

half of this activity is .... Bq,

which is at .... min

so the half-life is ....

....

Half-life = ... min

(3 marks)

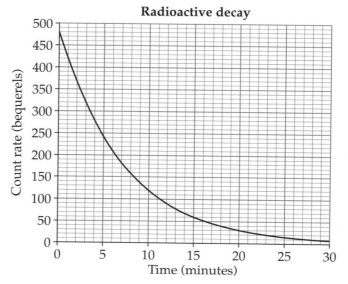

Radioactive decay

Count rate (bequerels) vs Time (minutes)

3 After the Chernobyl nuclear power station exploded in 1986, a radioactive isotope of caesium fell on northern England and Wales. At one place, the activity of a soil sample was 64 Bq in 1986. The radioactivity due to caesium-137 was expected to fall to 32 Bq in 30 years. The level of radioactivity in the soil today is higher than predicted. Discuss the factors affecting the accuracy of the prediction.

> Remember that a sample of soil contains many substances, some of which are naturally radioactive.

....

....

....

(3 marks)

Uses of radiation

 1 Gamma rays are used to produce images of the organs inside the body and to treat cancers.

> You need to recall the properties of alpha, beta and gamma radiation.

a) Explain why gamma rays can be used to produce images inside bodies.

....

....

(2 marks)

b) State the property of gamma rays that makes them useful for treating cancers.

....

(1 mark)

 2 A student says that some food is radioactive because it has been irradiated with gamma rays.

> Remember that 'irradiated' means exposed to radiation.

a) Explain why some foods are irradiated by gamma rays.

The gamma rays kill .... so that the food

....

(2 marks)

b) Some food is naturally radioactive, but the student's statement is incorrect. Suggest why it is incorrect.

....

(1 mark)

C-B **3** The level of activity of the background radiation varies in different parts of Britain.

The pie chart shows the sources of background radiation.
Explain the main reason why the level of background radiation is higher in some parts of Britain than others.

....

....

....

(2 marks)

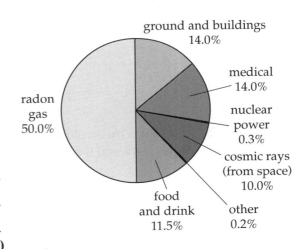

B-A **4** A scientist measures the background radiation count three times and then measures the activity of a mineral sample another three times. His results are shown in the table.

Test number	1	2	3
Background activity (Bq)	0.31	0.24	0.32
Sample activity (Bq)	2.63	2.57	2.60

> Remember to show how you work out your answer. Start by calculating the average background activity.

Calculate the corrected activity of the sample.

Corrected activity .... unit ....

(2 marks)

More uses of radiation

D-C 1 Machinery that produces standard sheets of paper uses radiation to check the thickness.

> **Guided**

You should recall the properties of alpha, beta and gamma radiation from an earlier topic.

a) Explain which type of radiation is used.

.... radiation is used because ....

(2 marks)

b) A radiation detector measures a sudden drop in the radiation that passes through the paper.

i) State the most likely cause of this change.

....

(1 mark)

ii) State how the machine responds to the change in activity.

....

(1 mark)

D-B 2 Look at the diagram of a smoke alarm.

The radioactive isotope americium-241 is used in smoke detectors like the one in the diagram. The americium-241 is a source of alpha radiation.

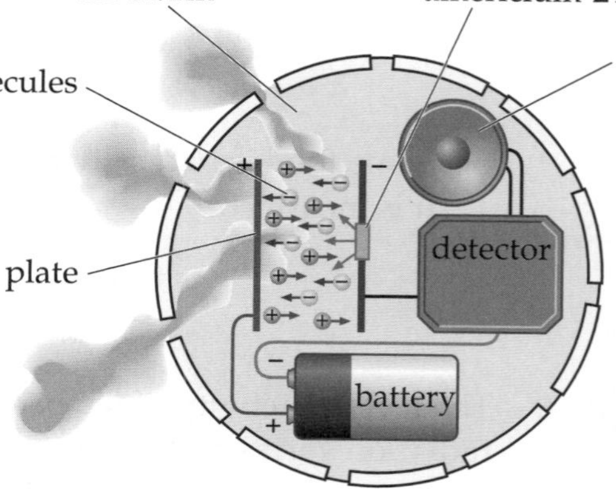

smoke entering the alarm
americium-241
siren
air molecules
detector
charged plate
battery

a) Explain why it is safe to use smoke detectors in the home.

....

....

....

....

(2 marks)

b) Explain why an electric current normally flows between the plates.

Remember that this topic is about the uses of **ionising** radiation.

....

....

(2 marks)

c) Explain why the siren sounds when smoke gets into the smoke alarm.

....

....

(2 marks)

B-A* 3 Engineers use a radioactive gas to trace leaks in underground pipes carrying natural gas across country. Evaluate the properties of the radioactive gas and the radiation it emits.

....

....

....

(3 marks)

Physics extended writing 4

Nuclear reactions, which occur in smoke alarms, nuclear power stations and in stars, involve the nuclei of many different isotopes. Discuss the different types of nuclear reaction that can occur, the causes and the products of the reactions.

(6 marks)

> You will be more successful in extended writing questions if you plan your answer before you start writing. In this question, you need to think about the different changes that can take place in nuclei and the various particles and products of the reaction.
>
> Some questions to think about are:
>
> - What can happen when an unstable nucleus decays?
> - What other reactions can nuclei take part in?
> - How can these nuclear reactions be started?
> - What are the products of these nuclear reactions?
>
> Remember that a good answer will include precise use of detailed scientific terminology.

....

....

....

....

....

....

....

....

....

....

....

....

....

....

....

....

....

....

....

....

....

Physics extended writing 5

A scientist investigates how the activity of a radioactive isotope changes with time. A trial run showed that the activity dropped to almost zero in a day.

1 Before removing the sample from store she measured the background activity. She took three readings, which were each different. She calculated the mean.

2 Then she took the sample from the store and measured the activity.

3 She repeated the measurement every half hour for six hours.

4 She converted the counts per minute to activity in becquerels (Bq) and subtracted the background activity.

5 She plotted the graph shown below and showed that the half-life of the sample is 1.5 hours.

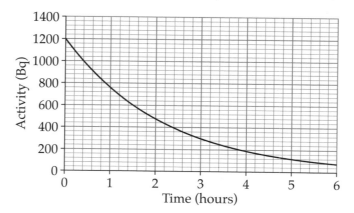

Discuss the actions taken in each step in the scientist's investigation.

(6 marks)

> You will be more successful in extended writing questions if you plan your answer before you start writing. In this question you need to think about why the scientist carries out each stage in the investigation.
>
> Some questions to think about are:
> - What is background radiation?
> - What is meant by the activity of a sample?
> - What is the half-life of a radioactive source?
> - How is half-life worked out from the data?

....

....

....

....

....

....

....

....

....

....

Biology practice exam paper (allow one hour)

Edexcel publishes official Sample Assessment Material on its website. This practice exam paper has been written to help you practise what you have learned and may not be representative of a real exam paper.

Fertilisation

1   During the process of fertilisation, sperm cells and egg cells come together to make a zygote.

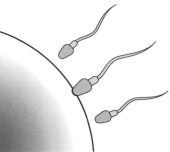

   a)   i)   What is the name give to sex cells, such as sperm cells and egg cells?

....

(1 mark)

       ii)   How are these cells made? Put a cross (⊠) in the box next to your answer.

☐ **A**   by meiosis to form diploid cells

☐ **B**   by meiosis to form haploid cells

☐ **C**   by mitosis to form diploid cells

☐ **D**   by mitosis to form haploid cells

(1 mark)

       iii)   State what is meant by the term **zygote**.

....

(1 mark)

   b)   In the developing embryo, tissues such as bone and organs such as the liver develop from stem cells.

       i)   Give the name of the process by which stem cells become specialised.

....

(1 mark)

       ii)   Using bone and liver as examples, explain the difference between tissues and organs.

....

....

....

(3 marks)

   c)   Give **one** way that adult stem cells differ from stem cells in an embryo.

....

(1 mark)

(Total for Question 1 = 8 marks)

Transporting water

2   Plants and animals have developed mechanisms to obtain and transport water, sugars and other nutrients.

a) Plants obtain their water from the soil.

i)   State the name of the cells responsible for absorbing water out of the soil.

....

(1 mark)

ii) State the name of the process involved in taking water out of the soil.

☐ **A** active transport

☐ **B** diffusion

☐ **C** osmosis

☐ **D** transpiration

(1 mark)

b) Plants use both xylem and phloem vessels for transport. Compare the roles of the two types of vessel.

....

....

(2 marks)

c) Soil contains low concentrations of mineral ions. Plants need to use a different process to absorb these mineral ions from the soil. Describe the process that is used.

....

....

(2 marks)

d) Our muscles need sugars to respire. The sugars enter the muscle cells from the blood by diffusion. The sugars enter the muscle cells from the blood. Explain how this process takes place.

....

....

(2 marks)

(Total for Question 2 = 8 marks)

Digestion in humans

3 The human digestive system is adapted to make sure that humans can extract nutrients from the food. The diagram shows the human digestive system.

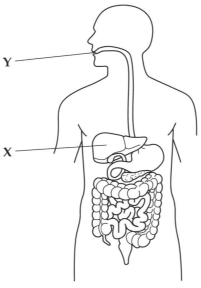

a) Name the part of the digestive system labelled **X**.
Put a cross (☒) in the box next to your answer.

☐ **A** gall bladder

☐ **B** liver

☐ **C** oesophagus

☐ **D** pancreas   **(1 mark)**

b) The digestion of one food molecule starts in the organ labelled **Y**.

i) State the name of this food molecule.

....
                                                                                                                    (1 mark)

ii) State the name of the enzyme that is responsible for its digestion.

....
                                                                                                                    (1 mark)

c) Bile is produced in the liver and stored in the gall bladder. Explain why bile is important in the digestion of fats.

....

....
                                                                                                                   (2 marks)

d) Most of the nutrients in our food are absorbed in the small intestine. Explain two ways in which the small intestine is adapted to absorb these nutrients efficiently.

....

....

....

....
                                                                                                                   (4 marks)

(Total for Question 3 = 9 marks)

GM fish

4 People with haemophilia have blood that does not clot easily. A protein called Factor VII can be used to treat people with haemophilia. Scientists have developed genetically modified organisms that produce Factor VII in their cells.

a) Complete this senctence by putting a cross (☒) in the box next to your answer.
Proteins are made by the transcription of sections of DNA called

☐ **A** chromosomes

☐ **B** genes

☐ **C** the genome

☐ **D** ribosomes   **(1 mark)**

b) The diagram shows the process of protein translation.

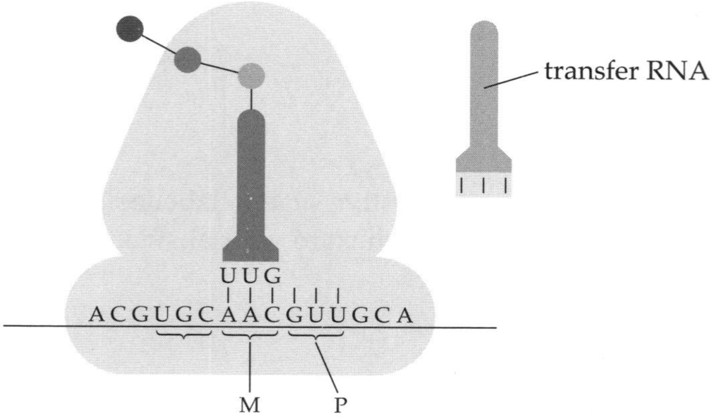

i) What name is given to the group of three bases in mRNA, labelled **M**?

....

                                                                                    (1 mark)

ii) Give the letters of the three bases that would be present on the tRNA molecule attaching at point **P** in the diagram.

....

                                                                                    (1 mark)

c) The GM organisms that produce Factor VII are made by genetic engineering. State an advantage and a disadvantage of using genetic engineering to produce the organism.

....

....

                                                                                    (2 marks)

d) To make large quantities of Factor VII, the genetically modified organism are cloned. Describe the process of cloning.

....

....

....

....

                                                                                    (4 marks)

e) When the Factor VII protein is extracted from the organism, it is given to haemophiliacs by injection, rather than as a tablet to swallow. Suggest why Factor VII cannot be given to haemophiliacs as a tablet.

....

....

(2 marks)

(Total for Question 4 = 11 marks)

Photosynthesis

5 Plants are described as autotrophic. This means that they are able to make their own food, rather than feeding off other organisms.

a) The process that plants use to make organic materials is called photosynthesis.

i) Which of these represents the equation for photosynthesis? Put a cross ($\boxtimes$) in the box next to your answer.

☐ **A** carbon dioxide + water → glucose + oxygen

☐ **B** carbon dioxide + oxygen → glucose

☐ **C** carbon dioxide + oxygen → glucose + water

☐ **D** carbon dioxide + water → glucose **(1 mark)**

ii) Photosynthesis requires a source of energy in order to take place. State the source of energy used.

....

(1 mark)

b) Some plants are grown in a greenhouse. Describe what would happen to the growth of the plants if the level of carbon dioxide in the greenhouse is continuously increased.

....

....

(2 marks)

c) The diagram above shows that the leaf has a waxy outer surface, which is waterproof. Suggest how removing this waxy surface would change the rate of transpiration in a plant.

....

....

(2 marks)

d) The diagram shows a section through a typical leaf.

epidermis ——☐ wax cuticle

stoma

Explain how the leaf is adapted to carry out photosynthesis.

....

....

....

....

....

....

....

....

....

....

....

....

(6 marks)

(Total for Question 5 = 12 marks)

Components of blood

6   Damian went to the doctor, because he was not feeling well. The doctor took some blood from Damian's vein to test.

The diagram shows some of the blood sample that was taken. It shows that Damian's blood has been infected by a microorganism.

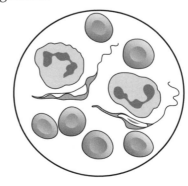

a) i) How many blood cells are there in this sample? Put a cross (☒) in the box next to your answer.

☐ **A** 2

☐ **B** 6

☐ **C** 8

☐ **D** 10

(1 mark)

ii) Describe the function of white blood cells.

....

....

....

(2 marks)

iii) The diagram does not show one solid component of blood. Describe this component and its function.

....

....

(2 marks)

b) The blood is maintained very close to pH 7.4. The regulation of blood pH is carried out by the enzyme carbonic anhydrase. The substrate for this enzyme is carbonic acid. Carbonic acid is formed when carbon dioxide dissolves in the blood.

i) State the part of the blood that transports carbon dioxide.

....

(1 mark)

ii) A mutation occurs in the sequence of bases when the DNA responsible for the manufacture of carbonic anhydrase is transcribed. Explain how a mutation in the DNA base sequence that codes for this enzyme may affect its ability to regulate the pH of the blood.

....

....

....

....

....

....

....

....

....

....

(6 marks)

(Total for Question 6 = 12 marks)

Chemistry practice exam paper (allow one hour)

Edexcel publishes official Sample Assessment Material on its website. This practice exam paper has been written to help you practise what you have learned and may not be representative of a real exam paper.

Transition metals in the periodic table

1 The diagram shows part of the Periodic Table.

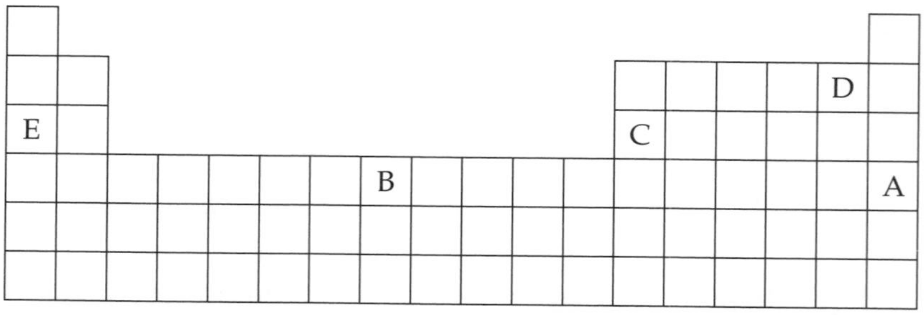

a) i) Which letter represents a transition metal? Put a cross (☒) in the box next to your answer.

☐ **A** E

☐ **B** B

☐ **C** C

☐ **D** D

(1 mark)

ii) Give **two** properties of a transition metal.

....

....

(2 marks)

b) Element A is in Group 0. State the physical state of element A at room temperature.

....

(1 mark)

c) Element C reacts with element D to form an ionic compound. The compound contains C^{3+} ions and D^- ions.

i) State, with a reason, whether C or D is a metal.

....

(1 mark)

ii) Give the formula of the compound made when C and D react.

....

(1 mark)

d) Describe how elements are arranged in the periodic table.

....

....

(2 marks)

(Total for Question 1 = 8 marks)

Rates of reaction

2 A group of students were investigating the rate of reaction between calcium carbonate (marble chips) and hydrochloric acid.

a) State which of these changes would increase the rate of the reaction. Put a cross ($\boxtimes$) in the box next to your answer.

☐ A adding water

☐ B decreasing the temperature

☐ C increasing the temperature

☐ D using larger marble chips

(1 mark)

b) The students added some calcium carbonate to a large volume of acid. They recorded the total volume of gas given off until all the calcium carbonate had reacted. The graph of their results is shown below.

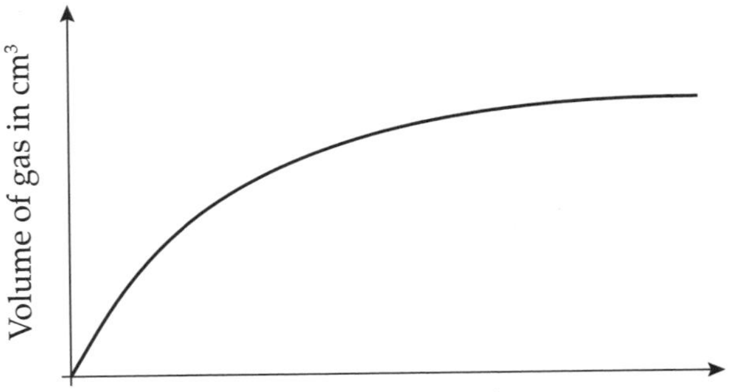

i) Sketch, on the same axes, the graph they would get by repeating the experiment with hydrochloric acid of a higher concentration.

(2 marks)

ii) Explain why changing the concentration of the hydrochloric acid has an effect on the rate of the reaction.

....

....

....

(3 marks)

c) Many cars are fitted with catalytic converters. Describe the purpose of these catalytic converters.

....

....

(2 marks)

(Total for Question 2 = 8 marks)

Burning methane

3   Methane reacts with oxygen in an exothermic reaction. The equation for this reaction is

$$CH_4 (g) + 2O_2 (g) \rightarrow CO_2 (g) + 2H_2O (l)$$

a) i) State the name given to this type of exothermic reaction. Put a cross (☒) in the box next to your answer.

☐ **A** combustion

☐ **B** dissolving

☐ **C** neutralisation

☐ **D** precipitation

(1 mark)

ii) What does exothermic mean?

....

(1 mark)

b) i) Complete the energy profile for the reaction.

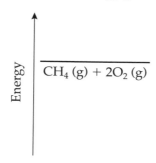

(2 marks)

ii) Explain, in terms of bonds, why this reaction is exothermic.

....

....

(2 marks)

c) In a reaction, 640 g of methane reacted with excess oxygen. Calculate the mass of carbon dioxide that would be produced in this reaction. (Relative atomic masses: H = 1, C = 12, O = 16)

Mass of carbon dioxide .... g

(4 marks)

(Total for Question 3 = 10 marks)

Testing for ions

4　A student is trying to find out the identity of a white solid in the chemistry lab. He carries out some tests to work out what the solid is.

a) The first test he does is a flame test. The flame turns yellow. State which ion this shows is present in the solid. Put a cross (☒) in the box next to your answer.

　　☐ A　calcium

　　☐ B　copper

　　☐ C　potassium

　　☐ D　sodium

(1 mark)

b) The teacher says that the other ion present is the carbonate ion. Describe how the student could test for the carbonate ion.

....

....

....

(3 marks)

c) The student makes a solution of the white solid and adds some barium chloride solution to it. A white precipitate is made.

A 2 g sample of the precipitate contains 1.39 g of barium and 0.49 g of oxygen. The remainder is carbon.

Show that the empirical formula of the precipitate is $BaCO_3$. (relative atomic masses: C = 12, O = 16, Ba = 137)

....

....

....

(3 marks)

d) Barium sulfate is an insoluble salt. It is sometimes used in medicine. Patients are given barium sulfate to swallow before having an X-ray of their digestive system.

　　i)　Give a reason why barium sulfate is used in this situation.

　　..

(1 mark)

　　ii)　Explain why the compound used is barium sulfate, and not barium chloride.

　　..

　　..

(2 marks)

(Total for Question 4 = 10 marks)

Atoms and isotopes

5 Atoms consist of a central 'nucleus'. Electrons orbit this core.

a) What particle (or particles) is/are found in the central 'nucleus' of the atom? Put a cross (☒) in the box next to your answer.

☐ **A** proton and neutron

☐ **B** neutron

☐ **C** proton

☐ **D** proton, neutron and electron

(1 mark)

b) A proton has a charge of +1 and a mass of 1 unit. Give the mass and charge on an electron, relative to those of a proton.

....

....

(2 marks)

c) The element rubidium has the electron configuration 2.8.18.8.1

i) Explain which group of the periodic table rubidium would be found in.

....

....

(2 marks)

ii) Use your knowledge of this group to state the reactivity of rubidium, compared with potassium.

....

(1 mark)

d) Not all atoms of the element neon are identical to each other. On average, 90% of neon atoms are neon-20 ($^{20}_{10}Ne$). The remaining 10% are almost all neon-22 atoms ($^{22}_{10}Ne$).

Explain, in terms of the particles present, how these neon atoms are different and why this leads to a relative atomic mass for neon that is not a whole number.

....

....

....

....

....

....

....

....

....

....

(6 marks)

(Total for Question 5 = 12 marks)

Halogens

6 Chlorine is a halogen and is found in group 7 of the periodic table.

a) State which of the statements about chorine is true. Put a cross (☒) in the box next to your answer.

☐ A Chlorine is a colourless liquid at room temperature.

☐ B Chlorine is a pale green gas at room temperature.

☐ C Chlorine is a pale green liquid at room temperature.

☐ D Chlorine is a red-brown liquid at room temperature.

(1 mark)

b) Chlorine exists as an element in the form of chlorine molecules, Cl_2. Draw a dot and cross diagram to show the bonding in a chlorine molecule.

(2 marks)

c) Chlorine reacts with hydrogen to form hydrogen chloride gas, HCl.

i) Write the balanced chemical equation for this reaction.

....

(2 marks)

ii) State the name given to the solution of hydrogen chloride in water.

....

(1 mark)

d) Explain how the properties of magnesium chloride, $MgCl_2$, depend on the bonding and structure of the substance.

....

....

....

....

....

....

....

....

....

....

....

(6 marks)

(Total for Question 6 = 12 marks)

Physics practice exam paper (allow one hour)

Edexcel publishes official Sample Assessment Material on its website. This practice exam paper has been written to help you practise what you have learned and may not be representative of a real exam paper.

Static electricity

1 A simple trick with static electricity is to rub a plastic comb on a woollen jumper. The comb can be used to pick up tiny bits of paper.

   a) Complete the following sentences by putting a cross (☒) in the box next to your answer. When the comb is rubbed it is given a negative charge. This happens because the comb:

   ☐ **A** gains protons

   ☐ **B** loses protons

   ☐ **C** gains electrons

   ☐ **D** loses electrons

   (1 mark)

   b) The pieces of paper are not charged. Explain why they are attracted to the negatively charged comb.

   ....

   ....

   (2 marks)

   c) If you try the same trick with a metal comb it does not work unless you hold the comb with rubber gloves. Explain why the rubber gloves are necessary.

   ....

   ....

   (2 marks)

   d) A similar method is used to remove particles of dust from the chimneys of power stations. Large insulated metal sheets are given a charge that attracts the dust particles flowing through the chimney.

   i) The plates are supplied with a direct current. State what is meant by a direct current.

   ....

   (1 mark)

   ii) A dust-collecting plate carries a charge of 360 coulombs. The collector operates for 1 hour.

   Calculate the current that flows between the plate and the dust.

   Current .... A

   (2 marks)

   (Total for Question 1 = 8 marks)

Nuclear fusion

2   One of the most important nuclear reactions that takes place in stars like the Sun is the joining of two hydrogen nuclei to form a helium nucleus.

   a) Explain why this reaction is described as an example of nuclear fusion.

   ....

   ....

   (2 marks)

   b) State a reason why scientists have been trying to carry out nuclear fusion reactions on Earth.

   ....

   ....

   (1 mark)

   c) The gases in stars are at an extremely high temperature. Explain why this condition is necessary for nuclear fusion to take place.

   ....

   ....

   (2 marks)

   d) State one reason why nuclear fusion has not yet been used as a source of energy on Earth.

   ....

   ....

   (1 mark)

   e) Martin Fleischmann and Stanley Pons announced that they had achieved nuclear fusion in warm water in 1989. Explain why scientists have not accepted their discovery.

   ....

   ....

   (2 marks)

   (Total for Question 2 = 8 marks)

Motion and force

3   A new rocket has been developed to carry cargo and people into space. It takes off vertically with a thrust of 4 000 000 N.

   a) State the force on the gases given out by the rocket.

   Force .... N

   (1 mark)

   b) The weight of the rocket at launch is 3 200 000 N. Air resistance can be ignored in the first few seconds of the launch. Calculate the resultant force acting upwards on the rocket.

   Resultant force .... N

   (2 marks)

The velocity–time graph below shows the velocity of the rocket in the first few seconds of the launch.

c) i) Calculate the acceleration of the rocket at launch.

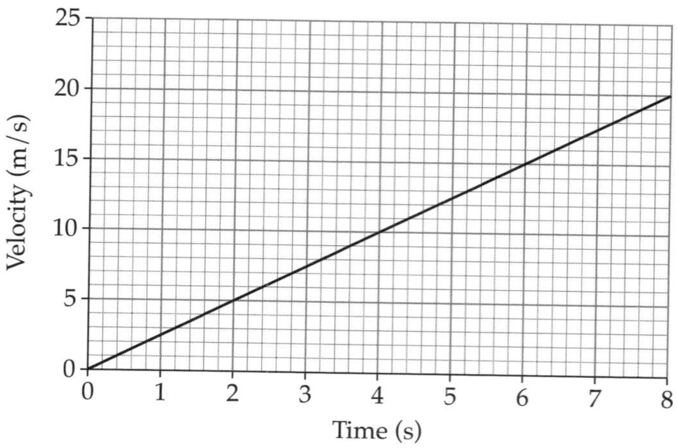

Acceleration .... m/s²

(2 marks)

ii) Calculate the distance travelled in the first 5 s of flight.

Distance .... m

(2 marks)

d) Describe two factors that will change the acceleration of the rocket after the first few seconds of flight, including the effect that they have.

....

....

(2 marks)

(Total for Question 3 = 9 marks)

Electric current

4   A student was investigating the relationship between the voltage and current through a filament lamp using the components shown in the diagram.

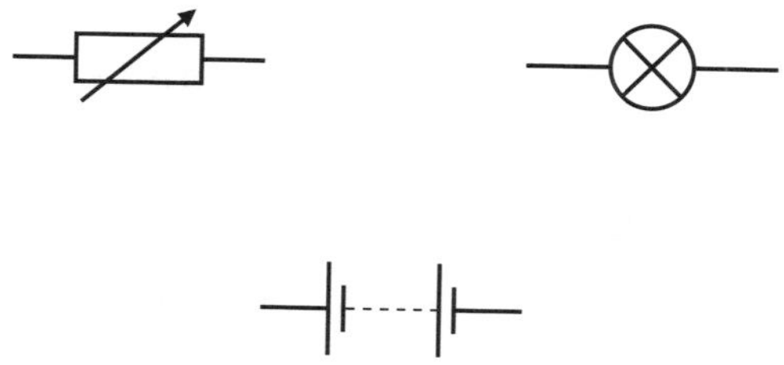

a) Complete the diagram showing how the student could measure the current through the lamp and the voltage across the lamp.

(2 marks)

b) The battery provides 12 volts to the circuit. At one setting of the variable resistor the current through the circuit is 0.1 A. Calculate the total resistance of the circuit for this setting.

Resistance .... Ω

(2 marks)

c) The graph shows the student's results.

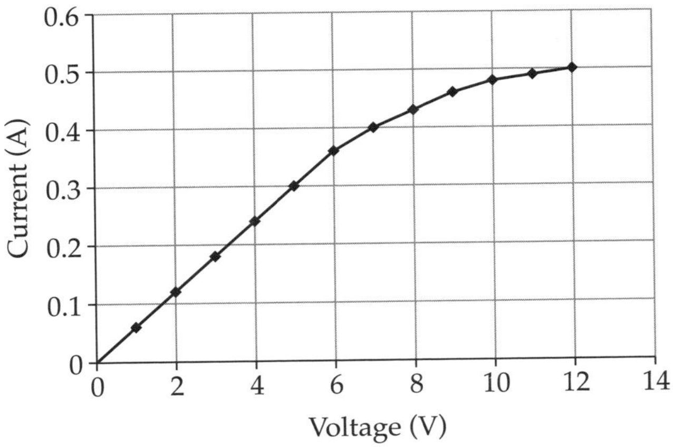

i) Describe how the current changes as the voltage across the lamp increases.

....

....

....

....

....

....

(2 marks)

ii) State the relationship between the voltage and the energy carried by the charge flowing through the lamp.

....

(1 mark)

iii) Explain the cause of the transfer of electrical energy to heat when a current flows through the lamp.

....

....

(2 marks)

iv) The current is 0.5 A when the voltage across the lamp is 12 V. Calculate the power transferred by the lamp.

Power .... W

(2 marks)

(Total for Question 4 = 11 marks)

Momentum and energy

5 In ten-pin bowling a player takes a few steps forward holding the ball. The ball is released and rolls along the alley.

a) State whether the final velocity of the ball increases or decreases when the player:

i) moves faster

....

(1 mark)

ii) releases the ball at a later time in the movement

....

(1 mark)

iii) uses a heavier ball

....

(1 mark)

b) A player holds a bowling bowl with a mass of 5 kg. She starts to push the ball forward horizontally and after 0.8 s the ball is released with a velocity of 2 m/s.

   i) Calculate the force that acted on the ball during the swing.

Force .... N

(2 marks)

   ii) The kinetic energy of the ball when it is released is 391 J. Which of the following shows the amount of work done by the player on the ball? Put a cross ($\boxtimes$) in the box next to your answer.

     ☐ **A** −391 J   ☐ **B** less than 391 J

     ☐ **C** 391 J   ☐ **D** more than 391 J

(1 mark)

c) Snooker, billiards and pool are games where a white ball is rolled to collide with a coloured ball of the same mass. The coloured ball should roll straight onwards into a hole. Skilful players can make the white ball stop when it hits the other ball. Often when less skilled players try the shot, both balls roll into the hole together.

Discuss the changes in momentum of the balls before and after collision and the forces acting when skilled and less skilled players set the white ball in collision with the coloured ball.

....

....

....

....

....

....

....

....

....

....

....

....

(6 marks)

(Total for Question 5 = 12 marks)

Radioactivity

6 Marie Curie discovered radium in 1898 while carrying out some of the earliest experiments on radioactive sources of ionising radiation. She took no special precautions when handling radioactive materials and her notebooks are contaminated with substances that are still highly radioactive. Marie Curie died from leukaemia, probably caused by ionising radiation.

a) Explain why scientists today handle radium in a different way than Marie Curie.

....

....

(2 marks)

b) Describe two ways that ionising radiation can cause ill health.

....

....

(2 marks)

c) Suggest precautions that are taken today when someone wishes to examine Marie Curie's notebooks.

....

....

(2 marks)

d) Radium has an atomic number of 88. The table below shows the properties of three isotopes of radium. Compare the structure and properties of the three isotopes and the hazards and penetrating power of the ionising radiation they give off.

Mass number of isotope	Type of radiation emitted	Half-life
224	Alpha and gamma	4 days
226	Alpha and gamma	1622 years
228	Beta and gamma	6 years

....

....

....

....

....

....

....

....

....

....

....

(6 marks)

(Total for Question 6 = 12 marks)

Periodic table

Key

relative atomic mass
atomic symbol
name
atomic (proton) number

| | | H hydrogen 1 | |

1	2											3	4	5	6	7	0
																	4 **He** helium 2
7 **Li** lithium 3	9 **Be** beryllium 4											11 **B** boron 5	12 **C** carbon 6	14 **N** nitrogen 7	16 **O** oxygen 8	19 **F** fluorine 9	20 **Ne** neon 10
23 **Na** sodium 11	24 **Mg** magnesium 12											27 **Al** aluminium 13	28 **Si** silicon 14	29 **P** phosphorus 15	31 **S** sulfur 16	35.5 **Cl** chlorine 17	40 **Ar** argon 18
39 **K** potassium 19	40 **Ca** calcium 20	45 **Sc** scandium 21	48 **Ti** titanium 22	51 **V** vanadium 23	52 **Cr** chromium 24	55 **Mn** manganese 25	56 **Fe** iron 26	59 **Co** cobalt 27	59 **Ni** nickel 28	63.5 **Cu** copper 29	65 **Zn** zinc 30	70 **Ga** gallium 31	73 **Ge** germanium 32	75 **As** arsenic 33	79 **Se** selenium 34	80 **Br** bromine 35	84 **Kr** krypton 36
85 **Rb** rubidium 37	88 **Sr** strontium 38	89 **Y** yttrium 39	91 **Zr** zirconium 40	93 **Nb** niobium 41	96 **Mo** molybdenum 42	[98] **Tc** technetium 43	101 **Ru** ruthenium 44	103 **Rh** rhodium 45	106 **Pd** palladium 46	108 **Ag** silver 47	112 **Cd** cadmium 48	115 **In** indium 49	119 **Sn** tin 50	122 **Sb** antimony 51	128 **Te** tellurium 52	127 **I** iodine 53	131 **Xe** xenon 54
133 **Cs** caesium 55	137 **Ba** barium 56	139 **La*** lanthanum 57	178 **Hf** hafnium 72	181 **Ta** tantalum 73	184 **W** tungsten 74	186 **Re** rhenium 75	190 **Os** osmium 76	192 **Ir** iridium 77	195 **Pt** platinum 78	197 **Au** gold 79	201 **Hg** mercury 80	204 **Tl** thallium 81	207 **Pb** lead 82	209 **Bi** bismuth 83	[209] **Po** polonium 84	[210] **At** astatine 85	[222] **Rn** radon 86
[223] **Mn** francium 87	[226] **Ra** radium 88	[227] **Ac*** actinium 89	[261] **Rf** rutherfordium 104	[262] **Db** dubnium 105	[266] **Sg** seaborgium 106	[264] **Bh** bohrium 107	[277] **Hs** hassium 108	[268] **Mt** meitnerium 109	[271] **Ds** darmstadtium 110	[272] **Rg** roentgenium 111							

Elements with atomic numbers 112–116 have been reported but not fully authenticated

* The lanthanoids (atomic numbers 58–71) and the actinoids (atomic numbers 90–103) have been omitted.

The relevant atomic masses of copper and chlorine have not been rounded to the nearest whole number.

Formulae

You may find the following formulae useful

charge = current $\times$ time $\hspace{8cm} Q = I \times t$

potential difference = current $\times$ resistance $\hspace{4.5cm} V = I \times R$

electrical power = current $\times$ potential difference $\hspace{3.5cm} P = I \times V$

energy transferred = current $\times$ potential difference $\times$ time $\hspace{1.5cm} E = I \times V \times t$

speed $= \dfrac{\text{distance}}{\text{time}}$

acceleration $= \dfrac{\text{change in velocity}}{\text{time taken}} \hspace{5cm} a = \dfrac{(v - u)}{t}$

force = mass $\times$ acceleration $\hspace{6.5cm} F = m \times a$

weight = mass $\times$ gravitational field strength $\hspace{3.5cm} W = m \times g$

momentum = mass $\times$ velocity

work done = force $\times$ distance moved in the direction of the force $\hspace{0.5cm} E = F \times d$

power $= \dfrac{\text{work done}}{\text{time taken}} \hspace{7cm} P = \dfrac{E}{t}$

gravitational potential energy = mass $\times$ gravitational field strength $\times$ vertical height

$\hspace{11cm} GPE = m \times g \times h$

kinetic energy $= \frac{1}{2} \times$ mass $\times$ velocity$^2 \hspace{4cm} KE = \frac{1}{2} \times m \times v^2$

Answers

Biology answers

3. Plant and animal cells

1 a) plants (1)
   b) X = vacuole (1); Y = chloroplast (1)
   c) contains DNA/chromosomes (1); controls functions of cell (1)
2 For each row, (1) for the tick/cross both correct, (1) for the role

Organelle	Plant (✓/✗)	Animal (✓/✗)	Role
chloroplast	✓	✗ (1)	site of photosynthesis (1)
cytoplasm	✓	✓ (1)	site of chemical reactions (1)
mitochondria	✓	✓ (1)	respiration/site of energy production (1)
vacuole	✓	✗ (1)	keeps plant cell rigid/stores water and mineral ions (1)

3 cell wall supports cell/helps keep shape (1); cell membrane separates cell contents from surroundings/controls movement in and out of cell (1)

4. Inside bacteria

1 Light microscopes magnify less than electron microscopes. The level of cell detail seen with a light microscope is lower than the level seen with an electron microscope (4).
2 a) nucleus (1)
   b) i) chromosomal DNA (1); plasmid DNA (1)
      ii) chromosomal DNA (1)
3 a) $100\,000/2000$ (1); = 50 times (1);
   b) i) light microscope: $2\,\mu m \times 2000$ (1) $= 4000\,\mu m$ (or 4 mm) (1); electron microscope; $2\,\mu m \times 100\,000 = 200\,000\,\mu m$ (or 200 mm, or 0.2 m) (1) (Note that there is 1 mark for using the magnification formula correctly, but only 1 as the same formula is used twice.)
      ii) He should use the electron microscope (1) as he will see much more detail/it magnifies the image much more (1).

5. DNA

1 chromosome = string of genes (and other genetic material) all coiled up (1); gene = section of DNA molecule/section of chromosome that codes for a specific protein (1); DNA = molecule containing genetic information (1)
2 a) double helix (1)
   b) i) cytosine, guanine, adenine, thymine (2 if all correct, 1 if only two or three correct)
      ii) hydrogen bonds (1); between complementary bases (1)
3 a) breaks down cell membranes (1); so releases DNA (1)
   b) DNA insoluble in ethanol (1); so precipitates out as a solid (1)

6. DNA discovery

1 Wilkins and Franklin were looking at X-ray patterns of DNA molecules (1). This was important because they saw that it was a helical molecule (1).
   Watson and Crick were looking at the data produced by Wilkins and Franklin (and other groups of scientists) (1). This was important because it allowed them to build a model of the structure (1).
2 a) gene = section of a chromosome/length of DNA/that codes for a specific protein (1); genome = all the genetic material in an organism (1)
   b) The genome has very large number of bases (1); needed many scientists to process and analyse large amount of data in a reasonable time (1).
3 Any four points from the following:
   Advantages: reduce incidence of some diseases by knowing which genes are responsible (1); develop new drugs by knowing how disease affects us (1); improve forensic science/crime solving by better techniques for locating genes (1); allow people to make better decisions/changes to lifestyle due to specific genetic tests showing they have a higher risk of developing certain diseases (1).
   Disadvantages: access to too much genetic information can lead to stress/depression if you are told you are likely to develop a particular disease (1); pressure not to marry/have children if you have a genetic defect that you may pass on (1); possible discrimination such as not getting a job if you have a particular genetic disease (1). (To score full marks, there must be a mixture of advantages and disadvantages.)

7. Genetic engineering

1 a) The human gene needed is the one for insulin (1); because it codes for the protein/hormone (1).
   b) Enzymes have two roles – these are to cut the human gene out of the chromosome (1); and insert it into the bacterial DNA (1).
   c) The bacteria provide plasmid (1) DNA for the process; the bacteria are useful because they produce large quantities of human insulin (1).
2 a) rice (1)
   b) introduced gene for vitamin A (1); to combat vitamin A deficiency/to prevent blindness caused by vitamin A deficiency (1)
   c) gene can move to 'wild' crops (1); reducing biodiversity (1)
3 One mark for each valid point. Full marks are only available if at least one advantage and one disadvantage is given.
   Advantages: can manufacture very pure product (1); can manufacture large quantities of insulin (1); as insulin is human insulin, few problems with rejection (1); overcomes need to harvest insulin from animals (1).
   Disadvantages: ethical issues over modification of organisms using human genes (1); possibility that GM bacteria may prove unsafe/harmful in the long term (1).

8. Mitosis

1 a) mitosis (1)
   b) B (1)
   c) C (1)
2 16 (1)
3 a) nucleus (1)
   b) chromosomes paired (1); 23 pairs/full set of chromosomes (1)
   c) 23 (1)
4 Any four from: chromosomes in the cell are copied (1); cell divides to give two genetically identical daughter cells (1); asexual because no fertilisation is necessary (1); this can take the form of tuber formation (in potatoes) (1); or the formation of runners containing cloned offspring plants (1).

9. Fertilisation and meiosis

1 a) haploid means half the number of chromosomes (1); gametes are sex cells (1)
   b) Human gametes can be sperm (cells) (1) or egg (cells) (1)
   c) During fertilisation two gametes fuse together (1).
2 a) i) 40 (1)
      ii) 10 (1)
   b) daughter cells have mixture of chromosomes/genes/DNA (1); from both parents (1)
3 mitosis = single division, meiosis = two divisions (1); mitosis = 2 daughter cells, meiosis = 4 daughter cells (1); mitosis = diploid/pairs of chromosomes, meiosis = haploid/one copy of chromosomes (1); mitosis = daughter cells genetically identical, meiosis = genetically different (1)

10. Clones

1 Order is: 1 Body cell removed from adult dog; 2 Nucleus removed from egg cell (1); 3 Nucleus from body cell placed into enucleated egg cell; 4 Electrical stimulus applied (1); 5 Embryo grows (1) (1 mark for step 2, 1 mark for step 5, 1 mark for middle steps)
2 a) nucleus removed (1)
   b) Any three from: nucleus removed (1); diploid nucleus (1); inserted into enucleated host cell (1); stimulated to divide by mitosis (1)
   c) surrogate (mother) (1)
   d) female (1); because the DNA used to make the clone came from female adult goat (1)
   e) provide useful products, such as wool (1); to make goods for export/sell for money (1)
       OR keep rare species alive (1); when threatened with extinction (1)

11. Stem cells

1 a) 775/1250 (1) $\times 100 = 62\%$ (1)
   b) Any two from: many embryos are destroyed in the process (1); each embryo is a potential life (1); there are other sources of stem cells (1).
2 Any two comparisons, for example: all the cells in an embryo are stem cells (1), but in an adult, stem cells are found only in some places such as bone marrow (1); embryonic stem cells can differentiate into many cell types/all diploid cells (1), but adult stem cells can only differentiate into one type of cell/limited types of cell (1). (You need to mention both types of cell for each difference to get the 2 marks.)
3 a) become specialised (1); to perform a particular function (1)
   b) body may destroy cells from donor (1); if they are too different from host (1)
   c) embryonic stem cells not differentiated (1); can turn into any body cell, so can help replace damaged tissue (1)

12. Protein synthesis

1 **a)** adenine (1); thymine (1)
  b) amino acids (1)
2 **a)** messenger (1)
  b) transcription (1)
  c) one (1); uracil (1)
  d) A (1)
3 **a)** sequence of 3 bases/base triplet (1)
  b) each tRNA molecule carries an amino acid (1); that corresponds to the codon on mRNA to the ribosome (1); tRNA aligns the amino acids according to the codons on mRNA (1)
  c) translation (1)

13. Proteins and mutations

1 A mutation can be beneficial, harmful or neither (1)
2 **a)** plots correctly plotted (2); line through the points (1)
  b) increasing dose increases mutations (1); (directly) proportional (1)
3 beneficial: may help prevent malarial infection (1); harmful (any two from the following): less good at carrying oxygen/carry less oxygen (1); sickle shape means that flow through capillaries is poor (1); less aerobic respiration happens in tissues/less energy released (1); so health problems e.g. poor response to exercise, bad growth, fatigue (1)

14. Enzymes

1 **a)**

Enzyme	Where it acts	Substrate
amylase	mouth/small intestine (1)	starch (1)
lipase	small intestine (1)	fat/lipid (1)

  b) The molecules that make up our food are large/often insoluble (1); enzymes help by breaking them down/making them smaller (1); the products of digestion are more soluble/easily absorbed (1).
2 Enzymes are not living (1); enzymes are proteins, not lipids (1).
3 **a)** protease (1); needs to break down egg stain, which is made from protein (1)
  b) enzyme is denatured/active site destroyed (1); at high temperatures (1); so would not work as well/less active (1)

15. Enzyme action

1 **a)** fat/lipids (1)
  b) increase (1); increase (1); no effect (1)
2 Starch would not be broken down/would be broken down more slowly (1); because amylase works best at alkaline pH/works best at specific pH (1); and active site might be altered/enzyme might be denatured at lower pH (1).
3 **a)** 60–65°C (1)
  b) higher temperature/more energy (1); increased rate (1). *An alternative answer might be: enzyme is found in high temperature environment (1), so enzymes are adapted to work best at 60°C rather than 30°C (1).*
  c) Rate of reaction decreases very rapidly (1); because the enzyme denatures (1); due to a change in shape of active site (1).

16 and 17. Biology extended writing 1 and 2

Answers can be found on page 132.

18. Aerobic respiration

1 **a)** oxygen and glucose (1)
  b) from high to low concentration (1)
2 Respiration is the release of energy (in cells) from glucose and oxygen (1); breathing is a mechanical process to inflate and deflate the lungs so that the body takes in oxygen needed for respiration (1).
3 **a)** glucose + oxygen (1) → carbon dioxide + water (1)
  b) capillaries (1)
  c) diffusion (1); movement of substances from areas of high concentration to areas of low concentration (1); oxygen – moves from blood/capillaries into cells (1); carbon dioxide – moves from cells into blood/capillaries (1)
  d) maintains concentration gradient (1); so that diffusion can continue to supply oxygen/remove carbon dioxide (1)

19. Exercise

1 **a)** Stroke volume is the volume of blood pumped from heart in a heartbeat (1).
  b) i) cardiac output = stroke volume × heart rate = 60 × 75 (1); = 4500 (1) cm³/minute
     ii) Cardiac output increases (1); then any two from: cells need to respire faster/needs more oxygen and glucose (1); more blood needed for respiring cells (1); so heart rate must increase (1).
2 **a)** 100 − 80 (1) = 20; 20/80 × 100 (1) = 25% (1)

b) most strenuous exercise (1); highest demand for oxygen/glucose/respiration (1)
c) rearrange equation to give stroke volume = cardiac output/heart rate (1) = 4000/50 (1) = 80 (1) cm³

20. Anaerobic respiration

1 **a)** lactic acid (1)
  b) increases (1)
  c) He had to run fast, so his muscles had more work to do/needed to respire more (1); he cannot use aerobic respiration alone because not enough oxygen can be delivered to cells (1)
2 **a)** lower for anaerobic OR higher for aerobic (1) (but often quicker)
  b) glucose (1) → lactic acid (1)
  c) The body needs more energy than aerobic respiration can supply (1); cannot get enough oxygen to respiring cells (1).
3 Any four from: oxygen consumption increases during exercise (1) but reaches a maximum value (1); no more oxygen can be delivered for aerobic respiration (1); increased energy needed comes from anaerobic respiration (1); lactic acid builds up (1); after exercise, excess oxygen needed to break down lactic acid (1); this is post-exercise oxygen consumption (1); so oxygen consumption does not fall rapidly after exercise (1).

21. Photosynthesis

1 **a)** C (1)
  b) chloroplast (1); trap sunlight/allow photosynthesis (1)
  c) collect more sunlight (1); needed for photosynthesis (1)
2 **a)** points plotted (2), straight lines between points (1)
  b) 78 cm (+/− 2 cm) (1)
  c) the greater the light intensity, the higher the rate (1); not a linear relationship (1)

22. Limiting factors

1 **a)** light intensity (1); temperature (1); carbon dioxide concentration (1)
  b) carbon dioxide + water (1) → glucose + oxygen (1)
2 **a)** Increasing the carbon dioxide concentration increases the rate of photosynthesis (1).
  b) The rate reaches a maximum (1); because another factor limits the rate (1).
  c) You could the increase temperature/light intensity (1) as this would make photosynthesis happen faster/more quickly (1).
3 Increased temperature increases the rate of reaction (1) so photosynthesis/growth happens faster (1); eventually other factors limit rate/rate reaches maximum (1); higher temperatures denature enzymes responsible for photosynthesis (1).

23. Water transport

1 **a) i)** roots (1)
     ii) leaves (1)
  b) Water is transported in the xylem (1); sugars are transported in the phloem (1). *Water does travel in the phloem but only as a part of the solution of sugars.*
2 **a)** transpiration = water loss from leaves of plant (1); due to evaporation from leaf surface (1)
  b) stomata (in the leaf) (1)
  c) i) moves faster (1); because faster rate of water loss from leaves (1)
     ii) moves slower (1); stomata covered so lower rate of water loss (1)

24. Osmosis

1 **a)** movement of water (1); across a partially permeable membrane (1); from high to low concentration of water (1)
  b) Having the same size potato pieces makes it a valid comparison/makes sure that the potato pieces have same surface area (1). (No marks will be awarded for just saying makes it a fair test.)
  c) The potato in the distilled water would be bigger/longer (1); the potato in the strong sugar solution would be shorter/smaller (1).
2 **a)** only allows certain molecules (usually small ones) to pass through (1)
  b) water moves into the tubing by osmosis (1); as higher concentration of (free) water outside than inside (1)
  c) root cells have hairs/large surface area (1); and have thin wall/thin membrane (1)

25. Organisms and the environment

1 **a)** use a pitfall trap (1); can be left overnight (1)
  b) use pitfall traps of same size (1); as area being investigated needs to be the same in each place that ants are counted (1) OR leave pitfall traps out for same time (1); so that there is the same chance for ants to fall into traps in each area being investigated (1)
  c) plot a bar chart (1)

2 Pooters are used because they cause little/no damage (1) to the insects, unlike a method like sweep nets; pooters are better for collecting small insects than a pitfall trap, as larger insects caught in a pitfall trap might eat smaller ones (1).

3 a) $(24 + 17 + 31 + 28)/4 = 25$ (1)
  b) $25 \times 100 = 2500\,m^2$ (1)
  c) 25×2500 (1) $= 62\,500$ worms (1)

26. Biology extended writing 3

Answers can be found on page 132.

27. Fossils and evolution

1 a) smaller (1); smaller (1)
  b) A (1)

2 Fossils do not usually form for soft tissues (1); because these tissues decay/rot (1); OR fossils do not always form (1); because the organisms are eaten/the soil conditions are not correct (1); OR fossils do not always last until they are found (1); because the rock containing the fossil is destroyed (1).

3 a) similarity – has 5 'fingers'/pentadactyl (1); difference – bat has wing/human has arm/leg (1); or differences in the relative lengths of different bones (1)
  b) Any three from: pentadactyl limb (1); common in all these mammals (1); simple version of this structure also seen in fossils going back millions of years (1); so very likely to have a common ancestor (1); and each mammal developed in a different way to adapt to its habitat (1).

28. Growth

1 a) C (1)
  b) $47.5 - 46$ (1) $= 1.5\,cm$ $(+/- 0.2\,cm)$ (1)

2 a) $15.35 - 12.75 = 2.60\,g$ (1); $2.60/12.75 \times 100 = 20.4\%$ (1)
  b) height (1); measured with ruler, ensuring stem is vertical (1); or size (1); by number of shoots/leaves (1)

29. Growth of plants and animals

1 a) tips (1); of roots or shoots (1)
  b) The type of cell division used for growth is mitosis (1). This continues until they are fully grown/mature (1).

2 a) mitosis (1)
  b) cell elongation (1); cells at tips of roots/shoots increase in length (1)

3 a) stem cells (1)
  b) become specialised (1); to perform a particular function (1)
  c) for repair of body tissue (1)
  d) Any two from: plants have stem cells that can differentiate into many types of cell (1); plant cells can differentiate throughout the life of the plant (1); adult human stem cells can only differentiate into some cell types (1); an arm contains a variety of very different cell types such as muscle/blood (so cannot be made from one type of stem cell) (1). (To get both marks, your answer must mention both plants and animals.)

30. Blood

1 a) nucleus (1)
  b) haemoglobin (1)
  c) Any two pairs from: large surface area/thin membrane (1); for diffusion of oxygen/nutrients (1); OR biconcave shape/flexible (1); to allow it to squeeze through capillaries (1); OR no nucleus (1); maximum space for haemoglobin/carrying oxygen (1).

2 carbon dioxide (1); to the lungs (1); OR urea (1); to the kidneys (1)

3 make clotting occur (1); stop bleeding (1); prevent microorganisms getting into body (1)

4 a) infection/disease/leukaemia (1)
  b) fight infection (1); then any two from: surround foreign cells/release (powerful) enzymes (1); create antibodies (1); to destroy foreign cells/pathogens/microorganisms (1)

31. The heart

1 aorta – carries blood from heart to body (1); pulmonary artery – blood from heart to lungs (1); pulmonary vein – blood from lungs to heart (1); vena cava – blood from body to heart (1)

2 a) right atrium (1); right ventricle (1)
  b) oxygen level (1); oxygenated on left, deoxygenated on right (1); OR carbon dioxide level (1); high on the right and lower on the left (1)

3 a) right ventricle (1)
  b) valve (1); prevents backflow of blood (1)
  c) has to pump harder (1); to get blood all round body (1); not just to lungs (1)

32. The circulatory system

1 This organ system is made of many different organs (1). They work together (1) in the organ system. The heart is an organ in the circulatory system. It is made up of several different types of tissues (1).

2 a) The aorta carries oxygenated blood away from the heart but the pulmonary artery does not (1).
  b) The aorta takes blood from the heart to the body/the vena cava brings blood into the heart from the body (1)
  c) The circulatory system is made up of the arteries, veins and capillaries plus the heart and blood (1)

3 a) pressure (1); high in blood leaving heart, lower in returning blood (1); OR carbon dioxide (1); low in blood leaving heart, higher in returning blood (1)
  b) Any four from: blood flows back in the vena cava (1); into right side of heart (1); leaves heart in pulmonary artery (1); oxygenated in the lungs (1); back to left side of heart (1); in the pulmonary vein (1); and pumped back to body through the aorta (1).
  c) Capillaries exchange materials with tissues/cells (1); so need thin walls to allow materials to diffuse/pass through easily (1).

4 can use diffusion (1); because they are single-celled so small distances to travel/because they have a high surface area:volume ratio/because the cell membranes are very thin (1)

33. The digestive system

1 a) A (1)
  b) mouth (1); small intestine (1)
  c) broken down to smaller molecules (1); more soluble/more easily absorbed (1)

2 oesophagus (1); muscles (1); peristalsis (1)

3 a) breaks down protein (1); into amino acids (1)
  b) i) bile (1)
     ii) made in liver (1)
  c) i) emulsify means breaking down fats into smaller droplets (1); so that there is a larger surface area (for enzymes to act on) (1)
     ii) alkaline/neutralises gut (1); products coming from stomach are acidic (1); enzymes in small intestine need alkaline pH to work (1)

34. Villi

1 One mark per complete row: starch – carbohydrase/amylase – simple sugars (1); protein – protease/pepsin – amino acids (1); fat/lipid – lipase – fatty acids and glycerol (1)

2 a) villi (1)
  b) diffusion (1); across membrane (1)
  c) need smaller molecules (1); to pass across membrane more easily (1)

3 villi destroyed/damaged (1); less surface area for absorption of nutrients (1); so less growth/respiration (1)

4 Any three from: thin membrane (1); folded to give large surface area (1); many capillaries so that lots of blood is supplied (1); and the flow of the blood maintains diffusion gradient (1).

35. Probiotics and prebiotics

1 a) This group is known as the control group (1); they allow the scientists to compare the effect of diet alone/diet with no statin (1).
  b) The effect of diet alone is to lower cholesterol (1); if statins are also taken, the level of cholesterol becomes lower (1); and the effect is greater than diet alone (1).

2 a) Lactobacillus/Bifidobacteria (1)
  b) Any three from: scientists evaluate data from clinical trials (1); where one group of people taking probiotics (1); and another group not (1); they can then compare effect on health/particular condition (1); look at evidence, not opinion/unjustified claims (1); evaluate if the data collection method described is reliable, i.e. provides strong evidence (1).

3 Percentage of women who reported IBS $= 35/750 \times 100\%$ (1); $= 4.7\%$ (1); not significantly different to 5% in normal population, so yoghurt makes no difference (1).

36 and 37. Biology extended writing 4 and 5

Answers can be found on page 132.

Chemistry answers

38. Structure of the atom

1 number of (negatively charged) electrons (1) is equal to the number of (positively charged) protons in the nucleus (1)

2 mass number is the number of protons (1) + number of neutrons (1); $4 + 4 = 8$ (1)

3 B (1)

4 The relative abundance of chlorine-37 is 24.2 (%) (1); relative atomic mass $= (35 \times 75.8 + 37 \times 24.2)/100$ (1); $= 35.48$, which is 35.5 to three significant figures (1).

5 The relative abundance of copper-65 is 31% (1); relative atomic mass $= (65 \times 31 + 63 \times 69)/100$ (1); $= 63.6$ (1).

39. The modern periodic table

1   vertical column – group (1); horizontal row – period (1); aluminium, sodium and chlorine – period (1); beryllium, magnesium and calcium – group (1); elements with similar properties – group (1)

2   a) O (1)
    b) B (1)

3   boron has 5 protons, 5 electrons (1) and 6 (11 − 5) neutrons (1)

4   a) The modern periodic table arranges the elements in order of increasing atomic number (1); tellurium has a lower atomic number than iodine (1) so comes before it in the table (1).
    b) Any three from: because of the chemical properties of these two elements (1); swapping them fitted the pattern better for repeating/periodic properties (1); puts iodine in the same group as other elements with similar properties (1); iodine has similar properties to fluorine and chlorine (1).

40. Electron shells

1   C (1)

2   a) 2 electrons in first shell (1), 8 in the second shell (1) and 3 in the third shell (1)
    b) aluminium (1)

3   diagram of electron shells around a nucleus (1); 2 electrons in first shell (1); 4 in second shell (1)

4   2.8.7 (1)

5   electronic configuration of sodium ion is 2.8 (1); this is the same as neon (1)

41. Ions

1   a) Ca^{2+} (1)
    b) F^- (1)
    c) Li^+ (1)
    d) S^{2-} (1)

2   a) 2.8 (1)
    b) a cation (1)

3   a) a chlorine atom gains an electron (1); electron is gained in the outer shell (1)
    b) Dot and cross diagram with: Mg^{2+} as an ion with a charge of 2+ (i.e. with 2 electrons on inner shell and 8 on the next shell) (1); oxygen drawn as an ion with 8 electrons in the second shell (1); the two electrons from magnesium to oxygen are drawn with the same dot/cross shape as for magnesium (1).

4   All have the same electronic configuration (1); 2.8.8 (1).

42. Ionic compounds

1   Any two from: the hydroxide ion is a compound ion which contains hydrogen and oxygen (1); together they have a single negative charge (1); the bracket is used when more than one compound ion is needed (1); Cl refers to a single particle so there is no need for the brackets (1).

2   magnesium bromide: $MgBr_2$ (1); sodium iodide: NaI (1); calcium sulfate: $CaSO_4$ (1); copper carbonate: $CuCO_3$ (1); aluminium chloride: $AlCl_3$ (1); sodium nitrate: $NaNO_3$ (1)

3   calcium hydroxide $Ca(OH)_2$ (1); iron oxide Fe_2O_3 (1); sodium sulfate Na_2SO_4 (1); copper nitrate $Cu(NO_3)_2$ (1); aluminium sulfate $Al_2(SO_4)_3$ (1); ammonium carbonate $(NH_4)_2CO_3$ (1)

43. Properties of ionic compounds

1   Sodium chloride is soluable (1); silver chloride is insoluble (1); magnesium hydroxide is insoluble (1); barium chloride is soluble (1); barium carbonate is insoluble (1).

2   C (1)

3   D (1)

4   Any two of: in solution the charged particles can move (1); moving charge is current (1); in crystals, ions cannot move (1).

44. Precipitates

1   a) $Pb(NO_3)_2$ (aq) + 2KI (aq) (1) → PbI_2 (s) + $2KNO_3$ (aq) (1) (plus 1 for the state symbols)
    b) i) a yellow precipitate/solid (1)
        ii) filter the mixture (1); wash the residue/precipitate/solid with water (1); and leave to dry/dry in oven (1)

2   Any four from: barium sulfate is insoluble (1); barium nitrate is soluble (1); the soluble salt would get into the blood stream and is toxic (1); the barium sulfate stays in the digestive system (1); which allows it to be photographed (1).

3   $CuSO_4$ (aq) + 2 NaOH (aq) → $Cu(OH)_2$ (s) + Na_2SO_4 (aq) ((1) for balancing and (1) for state symbols)

45. Ion tests

1   Add a few drops of acid to the sample (1); test the gas given off with limewater (1); limewater turns milky with a carbonate (1).

2   a) Dip a cleaned wire/damp splint in the powder (1); place in a colourless Bunsen flame (1); look for a yellow coloured flame (1).
    b) Carry out a flame test (1); if the flame goes red, calcium is present (1).

3   a) P contains sodium ions (1); Q contains calcium ions (1)
    b) chloride ions (1)
    c) Q might be calcium sulfate, carbonate, hydroxide or oxide (1); because all of these form insoluble salts with calcium (1).

46. Chemistry extended writing 1

Answers can be found on page 132.

47. Covalent bonds

1   one electron from hydrogen (1) and one from fluorine being shared (1)

2   four hydrogen atoms shown around one carbon atom (1), with each hydrogen atom sharing one of its electrons (1) with one electron from the carbon atom (1).

3   Each atom needs one extra electron to reach a full outer shell (1) (so they) share a pair of electrons/share one electron from each atom (1).

4

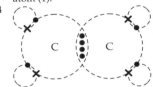

  Four hydrogen atoms shown around two carbon atoms (1); with each hydrogen atom overlapping with the outer shell of the carbon atom (1); one electron from the hydrogen pairing with one from the carbon atom (1); two electrons from each carbon atom shown where their electron shells overlap (1).

5   Any four from: each oxygen needs to share two electrons (1); but each hydrogen atom only needs to share one (1); so each oxygen atom shares with two separate hydrogen atoms (1); carbon needs to share four electrons (1); so each of two oxygen atoms shares two electrons with one carbon atom (1). *You can describe the bonding but you can also draw it.*

48. Covalent substances

1   a) Any one from: it is very hard/has high melting point/has high boiling point (1).
    b) In diamond, each carbon atom is bonded to four other carbon atoms (1); in graphite, each carbon atom is bonded to three others (1).

2   a) Simple molecular covalent substances have only a few atoms in each molecule (1); giant molecular covalent substances have a very large number of atoms joined together (1); OR simple molecular covalent substances are made up of individual molecules with weak bonds (1); giant molecular covalent substances are one large molecule (1).
    b) In simple molecular covalent substances there are only weak forces between neighbouring small molecules (1); but bonds (between the atoms) within molecules are strong (1); in giant molecular covalent substances the bonds are all strong (1).

3   simple molecular: conducting electricity poor (1); boiling point low (1); melting point low (1); giant molecular: boiling point high (1); melting point high (1).

4   Both have strong covalent bonds between the carbon atoms (1); which need a lot of energy (high temperature) to break (1).

5   They are simple molecular, covalent substances (1); because each fullerene contains a definite number of atoms in the molecule (1).

49. Miscible or immiscible?

1   A description to include: leave for time to settle/separate (1); diagram of a separating funnel (1); open tap and run through as much as possible of first liquid without letting any of second liquid through (1); remove beaker/collector and run little through until second liquid starts to come out (1); OR pour the remainder out through the top of the funnel.

2   a) water (vapour)/ice (1)
    b) carbon dioxide/dry ice (1)
    c) warm it slowly up to about −190°C (1) when nitrogen boils off (1); leaving liquid oxygen behind (1)

3   Any three from: nitrogen comes out from the top pipe (1); because it boils at −190 °C (1); oxygen comes out of the lower pipe (1); since still liquid at that temperature (1); evaporated oxygen condenses at top and runs down (1).

50. Chromatography

1   a) Dot movement depends on the solubility of the substances (1); not on the quantity of each substance (1).
    b) R_f value for tin is higher than for zinc (1) but lower than for copper (1).
    c) It is a fake (1) since there is no tin (1) and it contains some other metal (1).

2 $8 \div 10$ (1) $= 0.8$ (1)
3 $3 \div 0.6$ (1) $= 5\,cm$ (1)

51. Chemical classification 1
1 a) giant molecular covalent (1)
b) giant molecular covalent (1); ionic (1). *You could also include metals as an answer.*
c) ionic (1)
d) simple molecular covalent (1)
e) In giant structures, millions of atoms are held together by strong bonds (1); while in simple covalent substances, there are only weak forces between one molecule and the next (1).
2 a) High melting points could mean that the structure is giant molecular covalent (1) or ionic (1); if the melting point is low the structure could be simple covalent (1). *You could also say that a metal would have a high melting point.*
b) If an electrical conductor when molten then shows it is ionic (1); if an insulator then giant molecular, covalent (1).
3 Ionic bonds form when electrons are transferred from one atom to another (1); forming ions (1); attraction between ions is caused by positive and negative charges (1); covalent bonds share electrons (1). (If you have made any of these points using labels on your diagram, award yourself the relevant marks.)

52. Chemical classification 2
1 There are some insoluble substances in each group (1), so it does not help to distinguish between structures (1).
2 a) Metals are made up of positive ions surrounded by delocalised electrons (1); the electrons can move and carry the charge (1).
b) There are no charged particles that can move in the solid (1) so no current can flow (1); when molten or dissolved the forces holding the ions is overcome and the ions are free to move and a current can flow (1).
3 Put the sample in a beaker and test with an electric circuit that contains a bulb (1); test the sample in all three states (1); the bulb will light if the substance conducts electricity (1).
4 Any four from: in diamond all electrons are held tightly in the covalent bonds between carbon atoms (1); so no spare electrons (1); but in graphite each carbon is bonded to 3 others (1); leading to one spare electron per carbon which becomes delocalised/one is relatively free to move (1); moving charges are an electric current (1).

53. Metals and bonding
1 a) can be hammered into shape/shaped by compression (1)
b) atoms are arranged in layers (by metallic bonds) (1); layers have slid over each other (1) (either or both statements could be shown on the diagram – maybe with an arrow to show where you are talking about)
2 a) not fixed in any particular atom/can move about (1)
b) (charged) electrons are free to move (1); movement of charge is a current (1)
3 Any two from: in pure metals, layers can slide easily over each other (1); in alloys, the layers are less uniform/smooth and catch on each other (1); the particles of two metals are different sizes (1).

54. Alkali metals
1 a) Sodium: about 880°C (1) lithium: about 1340°C (1) (between 1320 and 1360 on the graph)
b) 690°C (between 670 and 720) (1)
c) moving down the group the boiling point decreases (1); OR moving up the group the boiling point increases
2 a) potassium + water → potassium hydroxide + hydrogen (1)
b) $2K + 2H_2O$ (1 for reactants) $\rightarrow 2KOH + H_2$ (1 for products); balancing the equation (1)
3 a) $2Rb + Cl_2$ (1) $\rightarrow 2RbCl$ (1) and 1 for balancing
b) Rubidium is very reactive (1); it must be prevented from reacting with air and water (1).
c) Any four from: Rubidium has more electrons than potassium and more occupied electron shells in its atoms (1); the outer electrons are further from the nucleus (1); the force between the negatively charged electron and the positively charged nucleus is weaker (1); it is much easier to remove the outer electron from a rubidium atom than from a lithium atom (1); so rubidium is much more reactive than lithium (1).

55. Halogens
1 Halogens are 2.7 (1) and 2.8.7 (1)
2 $2Na\,(s) + Cl_2(g) \rightarrow 2NaCl\,(s)$ (1 for balanced equation and 1 for state symbols)
3 The most reactive halogen is fluorine/at the top and they become less reactive going down the group/become more reactive towards the top of the group (1).
4 a) $Sn\,(s) + 2F_2\,(g) \rightarrow SnF_4\,(s)$ (1 for correct formulae, 1 for balancing, 1 for state symbols)

b) $2Fe\,(s) + 3Cl_2\,(g) \rightarrow 2FeCl_3\,(s)$ (1 for correct formulae, 1 for balancing, 1 for state symbols)
5 a) iodine is solid (1); astatine is solid as it is below iodine (1).
b) $AlAt_3$

56. More halogen reactions
1 $H_2 + Br_2$ (1 for reactants) $\rightarrow 2HBr$ (1 for products) (1 for balancing)
2 a) i) solution turns brown showing iodine is present (1); because chlorine displaces iodine (1)
ii) chlorine + sodium iodide → sodium chloride + iodine (1)
b) chlorine does not displace fluorine (1); because fluorine is more reactive than chlorine/chlorine is less reactive than fluorine (1)
3 add chlorine to colourless sodium bromide solution and it turns orange (1); showing that the more reactive chlorine had displaced the bromine (1); if iodine is added to sodium bromide solution, the iodine is unchanged (1); because the iodine has not displaced the more reactive bromine (1)
4 a) Gas is either fluorine or chlorine (either will displace bromine); after reaction, there is bromine present (as orange brown colour) (1).
b) either $2NaBr + F_2$ (1) $\rightarrow 2NaF + Br_2$ (1) or $2NaBr + Cl_2$ (1) $\rightarrow 2NaCl + Br_2$ (1)

57. Noble gases
1 helium is unreactive (1); so no risk of explosion (1)
2 a) radon (1)
b) C krypton (1)
c) A (1)
3 noble gases have full outer shells of electrons (1); so they do not gain, lose or share electrons (1)
4 Any four from: scientists were able to obtain nitrogen using chemical reactions/pure nitrogen (1) and also by fractional distillation of air/a mixture of gases from the air (1); the two samples had different densities (1); chemists developed a hypothesis that the nitrogen from air also contained another, denser gas (1); and carried out experiments to test this hypothesis (1); and discovered the presence of noble gases in the air (1).

58 and 59. Chemistry extended writing 2 and 3
Answers can be found on page 132 and 133.

60. Temperature changes
1 More heat energy is needed to break bonds (1) in copper carbonate than is released in making bonds (1) in the products; so heat is taken in (1).
2 Making bonds in sodium oxide releases more energy (1) than breaking bonds in reactants (1); so energy is given out (1).
3 a) Energy has to be put in (1); in the form of electricity (1).
b) $2H_2O$ (1 for reactants) $\rightarrow 2H_2 + O_2$ (1 for products) (1 for balancing)
4 Overall, energy is released to the surroundings by the reaction (1); because less heat energy is needed to break bonds in the reactants (1); than is released when bonds are made in the products (1).

61. Rates of reaction 1
1 a) $300\,cm^3$ (1)
b) 120 s (between 110 and 130 s) (1)
c) In the first 60 seconds the rate of reaction is steady (1); after 60 seconds the rate starts to drop until the reaction is finished after about 110 seconds (1).
d) steeper initial line (1); same final volume of gas (1)
e) less steep initial line (1); lower final volume of gas (1)
2 The rate is decreasing (1); because there are fewer particles to collide/solution is becoming more dilute (1); surface area of marble chips is decreasing (1); so less chance of collisions (1).

62. Rates of reaction 2
1 a) carbon dioxide/gas is given off
b) decreasing size of marble chips increases rate of reaction (1) by increasing surface area for collisions (1)
c) 1.3 (g) (1) (between 1.2 and 1.4); 1.3/4 (1); 0.3(25) (1) g/minute
2 a) large surface area (1), which speeds up rate of reaction (1)
b) Reactions are faster at higher temperatures (1); the temperature of the engine increases when it has been running for some time (1); so the catalyst works more efficiently (1).

63. Relative masses and formulae
1 mass of magnesium used = 0.25 g; mass of oxygen reacted = 0.16 g (1); Mg: 0.25/24 = 0.0104 (1); oxygen: 0.16/16 = 0.01 (1); ratio = 1.04 : 1 (round this to 1:1); so empirical formula is MgO (1)
2 a) 1.2 g/12 carbon = 0.1; 3.2 g/16 oxygen = 0.2 (1); (divide by smallest gives) ratio 1 : 2 (1) so empirical formula is CO_2 (1)
b) 15.6/39 potassium = 0.40; 3.2/16 oxygen = 0.20 (1); ratio 2 : 1 (1) so empirical formula is K_2O (1)

64. Empirical formulae

1 Relative formula mass of CH_4 = $(4 \times 1) + (1 \times 12) = 16$ (1); percentage composition of hydrogen by mass = $(4/16) \times 100$ (1) = 25% (1)

2 relative formula mass of carbon dioxide = $(1 \times 12) + (2 \times 16)$ = 44 (1); percentage composition by mass of carbon = $(12/44) \times 100$ (1) = 27.3% (1)

3 relative formula mass of nitric acid = $(1 \times 1) + (1 \times 14)$ + (3×16) = 63 (1); percentage composition by mass of nitrogen = $(14/63) \times 100$ (1) = 22.2% (1)

4 relative formula mass of $(NH_4)_2SO_4$ = 132 (1); two atoms of nitrogen = (2×14) and so percentage is $28/132$ = 21.2% (1); relative formula mass of NH_4NO_3 = 80; two atoms of nitrogen = (2×14) and so percentage is $28/80$ = 35% (1); relative formula mass of $CO(NH_2)_2$ = 60; two atoms of nitrogen = (2×14) and so percentage is $28/60$ = 46.7% (1); so the highest percentage composition by mass is for $CO(NH_2)_2$ (urea)

65. Masses of reactants and products

1 relative formula mass of reactant = $2 \times (2 \times 1 + 16)$ = 36 (1)
relative formula mass of oxygen = $2 \times 16 = 32$ g (1)
36 g water produces 32 g oxygen
1 g water produces $32/36$ g oxygen
0.36 g water produces $0.36 \times 32/36$ g oxygen = 0.32 g (1)

2 RFM lithium = 4×7 = 28, RFM oxygen = $2 \times 16 = 32$ g (1)
28 g lithium reacts with 32 g oxygen
1 g lithium reacts with $32/28$ g oxygen
5.6 g lithium reacts with $5.6 \times 32/28$ = 6.4 g oxygen (1)

3 a) RFM Al = 2×27 = 54 g, RFM iron = 2×56 = 112 g (1)
54 g Al produces 112 g iron
$54/112$ g Al produces 1 g iron
$54/112 \times 672$ g Al needed to produce 672 g iron
mass of aluminium = 324 g (1)
   b) RFM iron oxide = $(2 \times 56) + (3 \times 16)$ = 160 g (1)
160 g iron oxide produces 112 g iron
$160/112$ g iron oxide produces 1 g iron
$160/112 \times 224$ g iron oxide produces 224 g iron
mass of iron oxide = 320 g (1)

66. Yields

1 $(30/40) \times 100$ (1) = 75 (%) (1)
2 a) 0.08 kg (1)
   b) $(0.08/0.09) \times 100\%$ (1) = 89 (%) (1)
3 some acid will stay in the beaker (1) so less than 200 cm^3 of acid will react (with sodium hydroxide) (1). *There are lots of other reasons you could give such as not all the substances reacting or some sodium chloride being lost during drying.*
4 a) methane: 16, hydrogen: 6, (1); theoretical yield = 2.4 kg $\times$ $6/16$ = 0.9 kg (1); percentage yield = $0.8/0.9 \times 100$ = 89% (1)
   b) any one of: not enough steam (1); escaping gases (1); hydrogen might react with nitrogen or oxygen in the air (1)

67. Waste and profit

1 cost of transport to landfill/cost of land for landfill (1); cost of removing toxic gases/fumes before release into the air (1)
2 Three of: smells (1); danger (1); dust/dirt (1); increase in noise (1); increase in traffic (1).
3 a) $Fe_2O_3 + 3CO \rightarrow 2Fe + 3CO_2$ (1 for products and reactants, 1 for balancing); $2Fe_2O_3 + 3C \rightarrow 4Fe + 3CO_2$ (1 for products and reactants, 1 for balancing); $N_2 + 3H_2 \rightarrow 2NH_3$ (1 for products and reactants, 1 for balancing)
   b) CO_2 is a waste product which harms the atmosphere/is a greenhouse gas/causes global warming (1)
   c) Any two from: quicker reaction – more chemical made in a given time – bigger profit (1); higher temperature means more energy costs to maintain temperature – less profit (1); lower yield – lower profit unless re-use unreacted gases (1).

68 and 69. Chemistry extended writing 4 and 5

Answers can be found on page 133.

Physics answers

70. Static electricity

1 proton: charge +1, mass 1; neutron: mass 1, position: in nucleus; electron: charge −1, position: in orbit or around nucleus. (1 mark for each column correct.)
2 The negative charges on the balloon repel electrons (from atoms) (1) in the wall producing an induced (positive) charge (1) on the surface of the wall that attracts (the charges on) (1) the balloon.
3 a) Electrons move from the rod to the cloth (or the other way); (1) giving the rod and cloth (equal and) opposite charges which attract (1). (The answer must include the idea that electrons have moved/been transferred.)
   b) suspend one/both of the rods from a string (or any other method that allows the rods to swing easily) (1); (if they have the same charge) when the rods are close together, they will move apart/repel each other (1).

71. Uses and dangers

1 When the victim walked over the carpet he became charged/ gained electrons/lost electrons (1); when the victim touched the metal door handle the victim was earthed/electrons flowed from the victim through the door handle/from the door handle to the victim (1); this caused a spark (which ignited the gas) (1).
2 a) There could be a spark when the electrons move between the aircraft and the earth (1). (It is not enough to just say there will be a spark.)
   b) (Before refuelling) a metal wire/line is connected between the aircraft and the earth (1); this conducts the charge/ electrons or it discharges the aircraft (without sparks) (1). (Saying that the aircraft is earthed, without explanation, is worth 1 mark.)
3 a) So that the object attracts the (charged) droplets of paint (1).
   b) Any two from: less paint is wasted (1); the object is covered more evenly with paint (1); lower cost (1).
4 The (negatively) charged cloud induces (1) a positive charge (1) in the lightning rod; the rod attracts the charged cloud (1); the electrons travel down the rod to the earth (safely) (1). (Saying that charge travels down the rod, without saying electrons, does not get the last mark.)

72. Electric currents

1 a) An electric current is a rate (1) of flow of charge (1).
   b) charge = 4 A $\times$ 8 s (1) = 32 (1) coulombs/C (1)
2 a) electron (1)
   b) It is a direct current (1); the current flows in one direction (around the circuit) (1).
   c) $I = Q/t$ (1) = 15 C/20 s (1) = 0.75 (1) amperes, amps or A (1)
3 $t = Q/I$ (1) = 60 C/20 A (1) = 3 (1) s

73. Current and voltage

1 a) $3 + 5 = 8$ A (1)
   b) You could change the cell or battery to one with a larger voltage or potential difference (1). (You would also get the mark if you suggested changing the components to ones with lower resistances.)
   c) The electrons move around the circuit (or current is conserved) (1); so the current leaving the cell is the same as the current entering it (1).
2 a) correct symbols for the battery (or cell), lamp and voltmeter (1); voltmeter connected in parallel across the lamp (1)
   b) Volts = joules/coulomb so energy supplied = volts $\times$ coulombs (1) = 3 V $\times$ 10 C (1) = 30 (1) J or joules (1)

74. Resistance, current and voltage

1 current = 3 A; resistance = 7 Ω; potential difference = 3 A $\times$ 7 Ω (1) = 21 (1) volts or V (1)
2 a) straight line (1) through the origin (1)
   b) The line would be less steep (1) because the current is lower for the same voltage (1).
3 $R = V/I$ (1) = 2.4 V/1.6 A (1) = 1.5 (1) ohms or Ω (1)

75. Changing resistances

1 a) B (1)
   b) The current increases as the voltage increases (1), but the gradient of the line gets less steep/shallower, or there is a smaller increase in current at higher voltages (1).
   c) The current increases as the temperature increases (1); the change in current is non-linear (1).
2 The lamp lights up when the temperature is high (1); because the current through the lamp and the thermistor will be high when the resistance of the thermistor falls (1).
3 In the light the resistance of the LDR is low (1) so less current flows through the lamp (more current will flow through the LDR instead of the lamp) (1).

76. Transferring energy

1 When the charger is plugged in a current flows (1); energy is transferred to the resistor/converted into heat (1).
2 a) $P = I \times V$ = 5 A $\times$ 230 V (1) = 1150 (1) watts or W
   b) $E = I \times V \times t$ = 0.2 A $\times$ 4 V $\times$ 30 s (1) = 24 (1) joules or J (1)
3 a) $I = P/V$ (1) = 3 W/6 V (1) = 0.5 (1) A
   b) The current is the movement of electrons (through the wire) (1); when the electrons collide with the atoms/ions they transfer some energy to them (1).

77. Physics extended writing 1

Answers can be found on page 133.

78. Vectors and velocity

1 a) i) B (1) ii) C (1)
   b) distance = 60 m; time = 40 s (1); speed = 60 m/40 s (1) = 1.5 (1) m/s. (You can use any part A of the graph to read off the distance and the time as the line is straight, you should always get the same speed)

c) Displacement is the length and direction of a straight line between his home and the shop (1); but the distance he walked probably included bends and corners that he took (1).

2 a) speed = 84 m/24 s (1) = 3.5 (1) m/s (1)
   b) 3.5 m/s upwards or up (1) (the mark is awarded for the direction as long as the size of the velocity is the same as the speed given in part a))

3 time = distance/speed (1) = 400 m/5 m/s (1) = 80 (1) s

79. Velocity and acceleration

1 a) acceleration = change of velocity/time taken = 12 m/s/2 s (1) = 6 (1) m/s² (1)
   b) Running in a circle/around a circular track means she is changing direction (1), so her velocity is changing (1).

2 a) change in velocity = 30 m/s, time taken for the change = 5 s; acceleration = (change in velocity)/(time taken) = 30 m/s/5 s (1) = 6 m/s² (1) (You may not have drawn the same triangle, but you should still get the same answer.)
   b) distance travelled = area of triangle = $\frac{1}{2}$ × base × height = $\frac{1}{2}$ × 5 × 30 m (1) = 75 (1) m

3 $a = (v - u)/t$; 20 = (v − 0)/4 (1) = v/4 so v = 20 × 4 (1) = 80 (1) m/s (or, rearranging the formula first gives $v = u + at$ (1) = 0 + 20 × 4 (1) = 80 (1) m/s)

80. Resultant forces

1 Diagram with four arrows: vertical: down = weight, up = upthrust (arrows the same length); horizontal left to right = thrust or force from engines, right to left = water resistance or drag, the thrust arrow should be longer than the drag arrow. (1 mark for all the forces correctly named and 1 mark for the relative lengths of the arrows.)

2 a) The action is the weight of the cyclist (1) and the reaction is the (upwards) force of the bicycle on the cyclist (1). *The forces are equal and opposite.*
   b) resultant force = 30 N − 10 N − 6 N (1) = 14 (1) N
   c) The resultant force is zero/0 N (1), so the velocity is constant/stays the same (1).
   d) Only the resistance forces are acting, so the resultant force is backwards/against the motion of the bicycle (1); so the bicycle slows down/has negative acceleration (1).

3 a) resultant downward force = 1700 N − 1900 N = − (1) 200 N (1) (if you use a minus sign in your answer, as here, you must also state which direction you are using as the positive direction – downwards, in this case)
   b) The velocity of the probe towards the Moon will decrease (1); because the force produces an upwards acceleration/a negative acceleration (1). (If you do not mention the direction of the velocity or acceleration then you only get 1 mark.)

81. Forces and acceleration

1 a) The trolley will accelerate (1) in the direction of the pull/force (1).
   b) The acceleration is smaller/lower (1) because the mass is larger (1).

2 a) force = 3000 N × −13 m/s² (1) = −39 000 (1) N (1) (The minus sign must be included to get the first mark.)
   b) in the opposite direction to the spacecraft's motion/upwards (1)

3 a) $a = F/m$ (1) = 10 500 N/640 kg (1) = 16.4 (1) m/s² (1)
   b) The mass of the car decreases (1), so the acceleration will increase (1).

82. Terminal velocity

1 a) 2.5 kg × 10 N/kg (1) = 25 (1) N
   b) The force pulling/of gravity on the sack of potatoes is less (1) because the Moon's gravitational field strength is less than on the Earth/less than 10 N/kg (1).

2 a) C (1)
   b) The air resistance is equal to his weight/900 N (1); so the resultant force is zero (1) (and his acceleration is zero).

3 a) The Moon's gravitational field was the same for both objects (1); giving them the same acceleration (1). (Note: it is incorrect to say that the same size force acted on the hammer and feather.)
   b) On Earth air resistance (1) affects/slows down the feather more than the hammer (1) (You would probably get a mark for saying that the Moon is in vacuum but the Earth has air, but it is better to write about air resistance.)

83. Stopping distances

1 a) 12 + 24 (1) = 36 (1) m
   b) i) The braking distance will be longer (1) because of reduced friction (1) (between the tyres and the road) and so the stopping distance will be longer (1).
      ii) The thinking distance will be longer (1) and therefore the stopping distance will be longer (1) because the driver will take more time to react (1).

2 The students need to keep constant the mass of the block (1), the size or area of the block in contact with the surface (1) and the speed at which it is pulled (1).

3 The braking distance may have been greater than the 36 m that should have been sufficient (1) because: the car may have been travelling at over 40 mph (1); the car's brakes may have been worn/not working properly (1); the car may have been heavily loaded (so its mass was greater and the brake force was insufficient to stop it in the space available – remember that the stopping distances in the chart are for a typical car) (1). (Other valid answers will be awarded marks. Answers referring to reaction times and thinking distance are incorrect and will not gain marks.)

84. Momentum

1 momentum = 1200 kg × 30 m/s (1) = 36 000 (1) kg m/s (1) southwards (1)

2 a) momentum = 200 × 3 (1) = 600 (kg m/s) west (1) (600 on its own is worth 1 mark.)
   b) i)   momentum of Student 2 (600 kg m/s west) + momentum of Student 1 (0 kg m/s) = 600 (1) kg m/s west
      ii) Momentum is conserved (1); it must be 600 kg m/s west/the same (1).
      iii) 0 (1) kg m/s west
      iv) Student 1's momentum is 600 (1) kg m/s west
   (If no direction is given in any answer to part b) or an incorrect direction is given, 1 mark is lost.)

3 momentum of first skater = 50 kg × 7.2 m/s = 360 (1) kg m/s; total momentum after collision = 360 (1) kg m/s; so velocity = 360/(50 + 70) = 3 (1) m/s

85. Momentum and safety

1 a) The falling ornament has momentum (1); the damage is caused on hitting the floor because there is a large rate of change of momentum/force (1).
   b) When the package hits the ground the bubble-wrap squashes or crumples (1); so reducing the rate of change in momentum/the momentum reduces more slowly (2); or two points from: longer time of impact; momentum is reduced (to zero); force is reduced (1 mark each).

2 a) the mass of the trolley (1); the speed/velocity of the trolley (1) (just before impact)
   b) The longer the time the smaller (1) the rate of change of momentum/velocity/acceleration (1) so less force (1).

3 The seatbelt stretches, reducing the rate of change of momentum (2); or two points from: longer stopping time; momentum reduced (to zero); less force on passenger (1 mark for each).

86. Work and power

1 a) 4 N × 0.6 m (1) = 2.4 (1) J or joules (1)
   b) 2.4 J/3 s (1) = 0.8 (1) W or watts

2 30 000 J/2 s (1) = 15 000 (1) W or watts

3 a) $t = E/P$ (1) = 55 000 000 J/110 000 W (2) = 500 (1) s (1 for rearranging the formula correctly, 1 for changing the units to J and W, 1 for putting the numbers in the correct places in the equation, 1 for the answer)
   b) $F = E/d$ (1) = 55 000 000 J/80 000 m (1) = 687.5 (1) N

87. Potential and kinetic energy

1 a) GPE = 1.2 kg × 10 N/kg × 40 m (1) = 480 (1) J
   b) KE = $\frac{1}{2}$ × 1.2 kg × (80 m/s)² (1) = 3840 (1) J

2 a) GPE = 2000 kg × 10 N/kg × 0.5 m (1) = 10 000 (1) J
   b) 10 000 J (1) (or, the same answer as given to part a))
   c) KE = work done or GPE gained = 10 000 J (1 mark for recognising that these quantities are equal); $v = \sqrt{(2 \times 10\,000\,\text{J}/2000\,\text{kg})}$ (1 for rearranging and 1 for inserting the correct values) = 3.16 (1) m/s

88. Braking and energy calculations

1 a) change of momentum = 530 kg × 0 m/s − 530 kg × 25 m/s (1) = (−)13 250 (1) kg m/s
   b) F = (−)13 250 kg m/s/0.5 s (1) = (−)26 500 (1) N (If an error is made in part a) but the figure is used correctly in part b) the marks will be awarded. The minus signs show that the force is upwards while the craft is moving downwards.)

2 a) v = velocity of the car when it has stopped = 0 m/s; u = velocity of the car when it starts to brake = 20 m/s; F = (1300 kg × 0 m/s − 1300 kg × 20 m/s)/2.6 s (1) = −10 000 (1) N (1)
   b) The kinetic energy of the car as it starts to brake = $\frac{1}{2}$ × 1300 kg × 20² (m/s)² (1) = 260 000 (1) J; this amount of work is done to stop the car = 260 000 (1) J; distance travelled = E/F (1) = 260 000 J/10 000 N (1) = 26 (1) m (The mark in the last line can be awarded if an incorrect answer for part a) is used correctly.)

3 $E = \frac{1}{2}$ × 0.056 kg × (50 m/s)² (1) = 70 (1) J
   $F = E/d$ (1) = 70 J/0.01 m (1) = 7 000 (1) N

89 and 90. Physics extended writing 2 and 3

Answers can be found on page 133.

91. Isotopes

1 a) 22 (1)
   b) 10 (1)
   c) $22 - 10 = 12$ (1)
2 a) Both atoms have the same proton number/atomic number/number of protons (1); but they have different mass numbers/nucleon numbers/numbers of neutrons (1).
   b) $^{35}_{17}Cl$ (1) and $^{37}_{17}Cl$ (1)
3 They both have 8 protons/they have the same proton/atomic number (1) (in the nucleus); they both have 8 electrons (1) (around the nucleus); the first has 8 neutrons while the second has 10/they have different numbers of neutrons (1) (in the nucleus).
4 $^{39}_{19}K$ (2) (1 mark for the numbers 39 and 19 and 1 mark for them being in the correct places.)

92. Ionising radiation

1 a) An electron has been removed/lost by the atom (1); so the atom/ion now has a net positive charge (1).
   b) A beta particle is an electron that has a negative charge (1); it could be gained by the lithium atom (1).
   c) i) test 3 ii) test 1 iii) test 2 (2) (If only one type is in the right place – 1 mark)
2 Alpha radiation is more penetrating than gamma radiation (1); alpha radiation is particles, which get slowed down quite easily (1). Gamma radiation is waves which, are harder to stop (1).
3 Radioactive nuclei are unstable or in a sample there will always be some nuclei decaying (1); but decay is a random process (1).

93. Nuclear reactions

1 C (1)
2 a) ADEBC (All correct 2 marks, 1 mark for A and C at beginning and end, 1 mark for DEB in correct order in the middle.)
   b) In the uncontrolled chain reaction all the neutrons released can each go on to react/break up other uranium-235 nuclei (1), but in a controlled reaction only one neutron (1) is allowed to react.
   c) Daughter nuclei are the two smaller (1) different nuclei/nuclei of other elements produced from the reaction (1).
3 a) Nuclear fuel/uranium releases much more/millions of times the energy in fission reactions (1); compared with the combustion of the same amount of fossil fuel (1). *(Your answer should compare equal amounts of nuclear and fossil fuel. You should also show that you understand that fossil fuels release energy through burning but uranium releases energy through nuclear fusion; the answer 'Uranium has a much higher energy density', is also worth 2 marks)*
   b) Radioactive fuels give out energy for a very long time (1); which means that they can power the space ship for a long journey (1).

94. Nuclear power

1 a) One from: the products of the nuclear reactions/the daughter nuclei (that are formed by the fission reactions); materials from the core that have absorbed neutrons (1).
   b) It gives out ionising radiation (1).
2 a) i) They contain the nuclear fuel/uranium (1) which undergoes nuclear fission/release of energy (1).
      ii) They absorb neutrons (1) so the reaction is controlled/slowed down/so that fewer neutrons are available for the chain reaction (1).
      iii) It slows the neutrons (1) so that they are more likely to be absorbed (by uranium nuclei)/cause fission to occur (1).
   b) (The rate of the nuclear reaction must be increased) by raising the control rods (1).
3 The statement is not completely true because the nuclear reaction transfers nuclear energy as heat (1); in a coal power station chemical energy is transferred as heat (1); the other energy changes of heat to kinetic energy (in the turbine) and kinetic to electricity (in the generator) are the same (1). (The order of the statements does not matter.)

95. Fusion – our future?

1 a) The announcement was made in newspapers (1) instead of being peer-reviewed/validated by other scientists (1).
   b) The experiments should be repeated (by other scientists) (1) and would need to give the same results (1).
2 a) Small nuclei/hydrogen nuclei (1) are joined together to form larger nuclei (1). (An answer that just says that nuclei join together is worth 1 mark. Any answers that suggest that chemical bonds are formed between hydrogen atoms will not be awarded any marks.)
   b) Fusion in stars is joining nuclei together, fission in power stations is splitting of nuclei (1); fusion requires much higher temperatures/pressures/densities to start compared with fission, or the conditions for fusion are much more difficult to produce on Earth than fission (1).
3 a) very high temperature/over a million degrees Celsius (1) and very high pressure/density or a high gravitational field (that pushes the nuclei together) (1)
   b) The positive charges of the nuclei make them repel or electrostatic repulsion between the nuclei (1), so they need to be moving very fast or be pushed very close together (1).
   c) It is very difficult to maintain the high temperature/pressure or the reaction cannot be sustained for a long enough time, or the energy output (currently) is less than the energy input (1).

96. Changing ideas

1 a) At the time the dangers of radium were not known/recognised (1); so it was thought that it was safe to use (1).
   b) Evidence was collected (1); that showed that ionising radiation/radioactive material was harmful/caused illness (1).
2 a) wear protective clothing (a full description is not necessary) or work behind lead glass shield (1) (just wearing safety goggles is not a sufficient answer)
   b) use tongs or a robotic arm to grasp the material (1) (and hold it away from the body)
   c) carry it in a lead-lined container (1)
3 a) Ionising radiation can cause tissue damage (1); such as skin reddening/burns (1) (Other symptoms of illnesses caused by radiation are accepted such as hair loss, nausea, vomiting, headache, fatigue.)
   b) Ionising radiation damages DNA (in cells) (1); a single change to DNA may cause mutation (1).

97. Nuclear waste

1 a) i) LLW (1)
      ii) LLW (1)
      iii) HLW (1)
      iv) ILW (1)
   b) To stop the radioactive materials escaping for a long time (1) because the glass does not break down or decay (1). (To stop the radiation escaping is not accepted as the glass does not absorb the gamma rays.)
   c) It will have to be geologically stable or low risk of earthquakes (1).
   d) The rockets could fail or fall back to Earth (1), spreading radioactive material over a wide area of the Earth's surface (1).
2 a) Nuclear power stations do not release carbon dioxide (1) so do not contribute to global warming or climate change (1). (Nuclear fuel will last longer than fossil fuels (1) and so the electricity supply can be maintained (1) is also a valid answer.)
   b) People worry about the risks of nuclear power stations releasing radioactive material/ionising radiation (1), which could harm a lot of people or cause a lot of damage to the environment (1). (Mentioning the hazards of a terrorist attack, accidents such as Chernobyl, or natural disaster such as Fukushima will be accepted for 1 mark.)

98. Half-life

1 a) 8 million (1)
   b) 9.3 min is 3 half-lives (1); so there will be 2 million nuclei of thallium-208 left (1). (Over 3 half lives the number left are $16 \rightarrow 8 \rightarrow 4 \rightarrow 2$.)
2 The activity is 400 Bq at 1.5 (1) min (between 1.3 and 1.7 min is allowed); half of this activity is 200 Bq which is at 6.5 min (1) (between 6.3 and 6.7 min is allowed); so the half-life is $6.5 - 1.5 = 5$ min (1) (Answers between 4.7 and 5.3 min are allowed.) (If you used other points on the graph and got an answer of around 5 min you would get full marks. For this question, your 'working' can just be pairs of lines drawn on the graph.)
3 The prediction is based on the half-life of caesium (1); would expect that from 1987 to mid-2010s, radioactivity would have fallen to half this level (1); the level of radioactivity does not fall as rapidly because of the background radiation/radioactive materials in soil, which also decay (1). (Marks are awarded for discussion of the source of the prediction, i.e. the half-life of caesium, and recognising that other substances will release radiation in addition to the caesium.)

99. Uses of radiation

1 a) Gamma rays are penetrating rays/are not absorbed easily (1); so they pass out of the body (and are detected) (1).
   b) They damage cells/tissue (or they are ionising radiation) (1).
2 a) The gamma rays kill bacteria/microbes (and insects) in food (1); so that the food doesn't go off/turn bad as quickly (or increases its shelf-life or makes it safer to eat) (1).

b) When food is irradiated radioactive material is not added to it (1).

3 The level of radon gas in the air varies (1); because of different levels of uranium in the rocks and/or building materials (1).

4 average level of background = (0.31 + 0.24 + 0.32)/3 = 0.29 (1 for calculating either average); average level of sample = (2.63 + 2.57 + 2.60)/3 = 2.60; corrected activity = 2.60 − 0.29 = 2.31 (1) Bq. (*An answer calculated using incorrectly calculated averages will be awarded 1 mark.*)

100. More uses of radiation
1 a) Beta (1) radiation is used because the amount absorbed varies with the thickness of the paper (1). (Answers should show that thicker paper will absorb or stop more of the beta radiation. Answers giving valid reasons why alpha or gamma radiation are not used will be accepted.)
   b) i) The paper is thicker (1).
      ii) It adjusts the rollers to make the paper thinner (1).

2 a) Alpha radiation only travels a few cm in air/low penetration/strongly ionising (1); so no radiation escapes from the alarm (1).
   b) The alpha radiation ionises/charges the air (molecules) (1); the charged air molecules are attracted to the plates (completing the circuit) or the current is carried by the ions (1).
   c) The smoke (particles) absorb the alpha radiation (1); so the current decreases (and the siren sounds) (1).

3 Any three from: a gamma ray source (1); as the radiation has to pass though a few metres of soil (1); with a short half-life or a half-life of a few hours or days (1); so that the activity decays quickly (1); reducing risk of harm to people/animals (1). (Answers explaining why alpha or beta sources are unsuitable will gain 1 or 2 marks)

101 and 102. Physics extended writing 4 and 5
Answers can be found on page 133.

Extended writing answers

Below you will find a list which will help you to check how well you have answered each Extended Writing question. A full answer will contain most of the points listed but does not have to include all of them and may include other valid statements. Your actual answer should be written in complete sentences. It should contain lots of detail and link the points into a logical order. You are more likely to be awarded a higher mark if you use correct scientific language and are careful with your spelling and grammar.

Biology extended writing 1
Mitosis: in growth/repair/asexual reproduction; in body cells; two daughter cells; genetically identical; to parent cell; daughter cells are diploid; parent cell duplicates chromosomes; then divides. Meiosis: to make gametes; in reproductive organs/ovaries/testes; parent cells are diploid; replicate chromosomes; split twice; to make four daughter cells; which are haploid; and show genetic variation.

Biology extended writing 2
The gene coding for insulin; in the DNA; found in the nucleus; unzips; used as a template; to make mRNA; by complementary base pairing; this is transcription; mRNA contains uracil in place of thymine; mRNA travels through the cytoplasm; to the ribosome; ribosome reads the mRNA; in units of three bases known as a codon/triplet; this is called translation; each triplet codes for an amino acid; carried to the ribosome by a tRNA molecule; which uses complementary base pairing; amino acid adds to form a chain; called a polypeptide; continues until all 51 amino acids to make insulin are linked together.

Biology extended writing 3
Muscle cells need oxygen; for aerobic respiration; muscles work harder in exercise; so need more oxygen; and need to expel carbon dioxide; graph shows breathing rate increases at start of exercise; faster breathing rate increases rate of gas exchange; in lungs; increasing the amount of oxygen carried in the blood; this reaches a maximum; as blood is saturated with oxygen/gas exchange reaches maximum rate; so breathing rate remains constant; but muscle cells need more energy than can be provided by aerobic respiration; increased anaerobic respiration; build up of lactic acid; after exercise this lactic acid needs to be broken down; this requires oxygen on top of what is needed 'at rest'; so breathing rate does not return immediately to 'rest' level; but reduces gradually, as can be seen by less steep gradient on graph; EPOC.

Biology extended writing 4
This graph shows mass; weigh the baby; subtract mass of clothes/weigh baby naked; record result in kg; this graph shows percentiles; allow comparison across the whole population; the 'average' is the 50th percentile; about 7.4 kg; higher percentiles mean higher masses; e.g. 95th percentile is about 9.6 kg; 95% of babies have a mass of 9.6 kg or less; most babies should have mass between 5th and 95th percentiles; from 5.2 to 9.6 kg; if outside these ranges growth may not be normal; if baby changes between percentiles; especially by 2 or more percentiles; midwife could find other methods to measure growth such as length of the baby; or any other measurement of size, e.g. head circumference.

Biology extended writing 5
Oxygenated blood from lungs; pulmonary vein; into left side of heart; through left atrium; heart muscle contracts; forcing blood into left ventricle; valve shuts; heart pumps blood out to body; through the aorta; heart has two sides; with a dividing wall of tissue/septum; so blood cannot cross into right side; deoxygenated blood from body; in the vena cava; into right side of heart; through right atrium; heart muscle contracts; forcing blood into right ventricle; valves shut; heart pumps blood; through pulmonary artery; to lungs; to pick up more oxygen; blood vessels are separate.

Chemistry extended writing 1
Soluble barium salt needed; such as barium nitrate or barium chloride; soluble sulfate salt needed; such as sodium sulfate; suitable volumes; e.g. 25 ml; pour into a beaker; stir/mix; white precipitate forms; then take a filter funnel; with a filter paper inside it; pour in the mixture from the beaker; throw away filtrate/liquid that runs through the paper; wash residue; with distilled water; then dry; in an oven; word equation (e.g. barium nitrate + sodium sulfate → barium sulfate + sodium nitrate); symbol equation; which is balanced (e.g. $BaCl_2$ + $Na_2SO_4 \rightarrow BaSO_4$ + 2NaCl).

Chemistry extended writing 2
The description may depend on the alkali metal you have chosen, but the usual description would be: the metal floats on water; melts into a ball; moves around surface; with lots of fizzing; and sometimes the hydrogen given off catches fire above the metal; metal gets smaller as reaction proceeds; and there is a lot of heat energy given off/an explosion may happen; word equation e.g. sodium + water → sodium hydroxide + hydrogen; chemical equation which is balanced; e.g. $2Na + 2H_2O \rightarrow 2NaOH + H_2$; reactivity goes up as you go down the group; because there are bigger atoms; with more electron shells; so the negatively charged electron; in outer shell of the atom; is further way from the positively charged nucleus; and is therefore held less strongly; so more easily removed; to form an ion; therefore more reactive (it is also

acceptable to describe the reactivity decreasing as you go up the group, because the electrons are more strongly held to the nucleus as the atoms get smaller/have fewer electron shells).

Chemistry extended writing 3

In chromatography, the components in new additive; separate out; as the solvent runs up the paper; because the components dissolve in the solvent to different extents; to identify a spot in the sample, we match distance travelled by a spot; with the distance in the reference spots; or we can calculate R_f value; this is done using the equation R_f = distance spot travels / distance solvent travels; this is true as long as the chromatography is done under the same conditions; this gives a positive identification to the spots; example calculate; new additive does not contain E110; but does contain E163; spot from E120 is a little too high to be responsible for spot in new additive; so new additive contains E101.

Chemistry extended writing 4

Water is one of the reactants; it should be measured in a measuring cylinder; suitable volume e.g. 50cm^3; place the water in a polystyrene cup; and then put this in a glass beaker; to stop it falling over; put a lid on the cup; use a thermometer; ideally to measure to nearest 0.5°C or better; measure initial temperature of water; weigh out the ammonium chloride; a suitable mass would be something like 2 g; add the solid to the water; stir; until ammonium chloride dissolves; wait until temperature has stopped going down; measure new temperature of the water; repeat the experiment; with fresh water; but same volume of water; and same mass of ammonium chloride each time; until at least two measurements are the same; OR repeat at least 3 times; discard any results that are very different from the others; calculate a mean/average temperature change.

Chemistry extended writing 5

Particles of the reacting substances collide; and this leads to a reaction taking place; increasing concentration (of the acid) increases rate of reaction; because there are more particles; in the same volume of the acid; therefore, the chance of collision increases; because the particles are closer together; although there is the same chance of any collision being successful; the fact there is an increased collision frequency; means there is an increased number of successful collisions; if particles collide with low energy; no reaction takes place; increasing temperature; increases the rate of reaction; because particles now have more energy; and will move faster; this means that they collide more frequently; and these collision will take place with more energy; so they are more likely to be successful.

Physics extended writing 1

A current is a flow of charge; electrons carry the charge; the voltage or potential difference is the energy transferred per unit of charge (or 1 volt = 1 joule per coulomb); the current through a resistor is the voltage/resistance; current through heater = 230/53; = 4.3 A; an electric current in a resistor transfers electrical energy to heat; the energy transfer in the resistor is the result of collisions; between electrons and ions in the lattice; the energy transferred per second is the current × voltage; energy transferred = 4.3 × 230; = 989 J; which is nearly 1 kJ.

Physics extended writing 2

Car A has the higher acceleration; because it has the steeper slope at the start; Car B reaches the higher velocity; the acceleration is given by the gradient of the line; acceleration is the rate of change of velocity; the acceleration of car A = (40 − 0)/5 = 8 m/s^2; the acceleration of car B = (50 − 0)/10 = 5 m/s^2; the distance travelled is the area under the line; area of rectangle at constant velocity (base × height); area of triangle when accelerating ($\frac{1}{2}$ × base × height); Car A travels

$\frac{1}{2}$ × (5 × 40) = 100 m when accelerating; and 40 × 22.5 = 900 m; total = 100 + 900 = 1000 m before braking; Car B travels $\frac{1}{2}$ × (10 × 50) = 250 m; and 50 × 15 = 750 m; total = 250 + 750 = 1000 m before braking; Car B won the race; because it covers the 1000 m in 25 s compared with 27.5 s for car A; because it brakes first; the resultant force on car A is the highest at the start (same mass but higher acceleration); Car B has the greater momentum (higher velocity).

Physics extended writing 3

The kinetic energy of the cricket ball is higher because it has the greater mass; kinetic energy of the cricket ball = $\frac{1}{2}$ × 0.15 × 45^2 = 152 J; kinetic energy of the tennis ball is = $\frac{1}{2}$ × 0.56 × 45^2 = 57 J; the work done to stop the balls is equal to their kinetic energy; the force required to stop the cricket ball is higher; because it has a higher energy; and because it stops in a shorter distance; the tennis ball takes longer to stop because it crumples/compresses a greater distance; the rate of change momentum of the cricket ball is the greater; because the change in momentum is greater and the time taken is shorter; force to stop cricket ball = work done/distance moved by the force = 152/0.001 = 150 000 N; force to stop tennis ball = work done/distance moved by the force= 57/0.02 = 2 850 N; momentum of cricket ball = 0.15 × 45 = 6.75 kg m/s; momentum of tennis ball = 0.056 × 45 = 2.52 kg m/s.

Physics extended writing 4

An unstable nucleus can decay; giving out alpha, beta and/or gamma radiation; alpha radiation is a helium nucleus or 2 protons + 2 neutrons; beta radiation is electrons; gamma radiation is high frequency electromagnetic waves; radioactive decay is a spontaneous or random process; cannot predict when a nucleus will decay; fission occurs when an unstable nucleus splits into two smaller nuclei or daughter nuclei; uranium-235 undergoes fission; fission occurs when the unstable nucleus is hit by a neutron; fission of a nucleus also produces two or more neutrons; these neutrons can go on to cause a chain reaction; fusion occurs when small nuclei join together to form larger nuclei; hydrogen/deuterium/tritium nuclei can fuse; for nuclei to fuse they must overcome the electrostatic forces repelling them; hence the nuclei must be travelling at very high speeds; fusion only occurs at very high temperature and pressures/density or does not occur at low temperature and pressure; all nuclear reactions give out energy; fusion produces the most energy, followed by fission.

Physics extended writing 5

Step 1: Background count measures radiation from radioactive sources in the environment; 2 or 3 named sources of background radiation; the background count varies (with time) because radioactivity is a random process; the mean background count stays approximately the same in any place; a single reading of the background may not be accurate; the mean of at least 3 values gives a figure close to the true value of the measurement.

Step 2: The sample must be kept in a store to stop it interfering with the background count.

Step 3: The readings must be taken frequently enough to show how the activity changes with time; and over a long enough period to measure for at least one half life.

Step 4: Activity in becquerels is the number of nuclear decays per second; the background activity must be subtracted from the experimental data to give the true activity of the sample.

Step 5: The graph is a downwards/concave curve; the activity of the sample decreases but never disappears completely; the half-life of a radioisotope is the time taken for the activity to fall to a half of its value or the time taken for half of the nuclei to decay; the time when individual nuclei decay cannot be predicted; the half-life of an isotope is constant; illustration of how the half-life is calculated to be 1.5 hours (may be lines drawn on the graph).

Biology practice exam

1 a) i) gametes (1)
      ii) B (1)
      iii) fertilised egg (1)
   b) i) differentiation (1)
      ii) tissue = collection of cells of the same type (1); organ = collection of tissues working together to carry out a function (1); bone = tissue, liver = organ (1)
   c) Adult stem cells only specialise into some types of cell/partly differentiated/only occur in some tissues (1).

2 a) i) root hair cells (1)
      ii) C (1)
   b) xylem for water, phloem for sugars (1); xylem transports to the leaves, phloem can transport to and from leaves (1)
   c) active transport (1); uses energy/goes against concentration gradient (1)
   d) sugar molecules move from high concentration (in blood) to low (in cells)/down concentration gradient (1); across cell membrane/partially permeable membrane (1)

3 a) B (1)
   b) i) starch (1)
      ii) amylase (1)
   c) Any two from: emulsifies fat/breaks fat into droplets (1); larger surface area (for lipase to act on) (1); provides correct pH for enzyme activity/helps neutralise acidity (1).
   d) Any two answers, each worth two marks, from: villi (1), provide a large surface area for absorption (1); thin membrane (1), to make diffusion faster (1); rich blood supply (1), to remove digestion products quickly/take them to tissues/maintains concentration gradient (1).

4 a) B (1)
   b) i) codon (1)
      ii) CAA (1)
   c) advantage: large amounts can be produced/can make a pure product (1); disadvantage: have to kill the organism to get it (1)
   d) enucleated egg cell from host organism (1); insert DNA from body cell of the GM organism (1); shock cell to start division (1); place in surrogate parent (1)
   e) (protein) digested/broken down/made inactive (1); in the stomach/by proteases (1)

5 a) i) A (1)
      ii) (sun)light (1)
   b) increases (1); up to a maximum/until another factor is limiting rate (1)
   c) Water would evaporate from surface of leaf more quickly (1); so rate of transpiration would increase (1).
   d) cells in lower part of leaf are irregularly packed; leads to air spaces in the leaf; giving a large surface area; this allows more rapid gas exchange; chloroplasts; contain chlorophyll; for photosynthesis; more chloroplasts in cells on the upper surface of the leaf; stomata; on lower surface of the leaf; are surrounded by guard cells; to control opening; this allows air in; and waste products out; the rate of loss of water vapour (through the stomata); controls the rate of transpiration (6).

6 a) i) C (1)
      ii) surrounds pathogen/microorganism/foreign cell (1); releases enzymes/digests it (1); OR produces antibodies (1); which help destroy microorganisms (1)
      iii) platelets (1); helps blood to clot (1)
   b) i) plasma (1)
      ii) carbonic anhydrase is a protein; (change in base sequence gives) different codon; which leads to different amino acid in the protein; so may change the way it folds; leading to a different shape; this may affect active site; causing change in its shape; because the active site is specific; for carbonic acid/the substrate; and enzymes work on a 'lock and key'; the active site may now not fit substrate/carbon dioxide; at all; so no activity; or fit is much worse; so reduced enzyme activity; pH regulation compromised; possible that mutation does not change active site; and enzyme should function normally/be more active (6).

Chemistry practice exam

1 a) i) B (1)
      ii) high melting/boiling point (1); have coloured compounds (1). *Used in catalysts would also be an acceptable answer.*
   b) gas (1)
   c) i) C is metal because it loses electrons/forms +ve ions (1)
      ii) CD_3 (1)
   d) increasing atomic number (1); elements with similar properties in columns/groups OR each new row/period shows elements starting a new electron shell (1)

2 a) A (1)
   b) i) steeper gradient (1); but finishing at same total volume (1)
      ii) increased number of particles in the same volume (1); collisions (1); more frequent (1)
   c) increase the rate of changing carbon monoxide/unburned petrol (1); into carbon dioxide/water (1)

3 a) i) A (1)
      ii) heat is given off (1)
   b) i) line at lower level (1); labelled with products (1). *You could also add an arrow pointing down from the products to the reactant.*
      ii) more energy is released when new bonds are made in the products (1); than was required to break bonds in the reactants (1) (allow 1 mark for the idea that weak bonds are broken and stronger bonds are made)
   c) Relative formula mass of methane = 16 and RFM of carbon dioxide = 44 (1); ratio methane to carbon dioxide = 1:1 (1); 640/16 × 44 (1); 1760 g (1); OR Relative formula mass of methane = 16 and RFM of carbon dioxide = 44 (1); 16 g of methane produces 44 g of carbon dioxide (1), 1 g of methane produces 2.75 g of carbon dioxide, and so 640 g of methane would produce 640 × 2.75 g (1) = 1760 g of carbon dioxide (1).

4 a) D (1)
   b) add hydrochloric acid (1); bubble gas produced into limewater (1); which goes cloudy/milky (1)
   c) mass of carbon = 2 − 1.39 − 0.49 = 0.12 g (1); mass/relative atomic mass of Ba = 1.39/137, for C = 0.12 /12 and for O = 0.49/16 (1); ratio is 0.01 : 0.01 : 0.03, or 1 : 1 : 3 (1)
   d) i) opaque to X-rays (1)
      ii) barium sulfate is insoluble (1); so is not toxic (1); OR barium chloride is soluble (1) so would be toxic to the patient (1)

5 a) A (1)
   b) charge = −1 (1); mass = 1/1840 (1/2000 is also acceptable) (1)
   c) i) Group 1 (1); because it has 1 electron in outer shell (1)
      ii) more reactive than potassium (1)
   d) Neon has an atomic number of 10; so all neon atoms contain 10 protons; and they also contain 10 electrons; neon-20 and neon-22 have different numbers of neutrons; and are known as isotopes of each other; the number of neutrons is the mass number minus the atomic number; which is 10 for neon-20; and 12 for neon-22; the A_r of a neon is the average mass of an atom of the element; compared to mass of one atom of carbon-12; which is defined as exactly 12; to find the A_r we calculate the average mass across all isotopes; and, as not all neon atoms are same mass; the average is unlikely to be whole number; this calculation involves multiplying the mass number by the abundance and dividing by the total abundance; i.e. (20 × 90) + (22 × 10)/100; = 20.2 (6).

6 a) B (1)
   b)

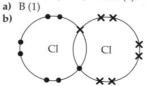

two electrons shared between the Cl atoms (1); each chlorine also has 6 unbonded electrons in its outer shell (1)

c) i) $H_2 + Cl_2 \rightarrow 2HCl$ (chemical formulae all correct (1); 2 put into balance (1))

ii) hydrochloric acid (1)

d) The bonding in magnesium chloride is ionic; because magnesium chloride contains magnesium ions and chloride ions; magnesium ions have a positive charge; of 2+; chloride ions have a negative charge; of 1−; both ions have full outer shells of electrons; because an electron is transferred; from a magnesium atom to a chloride atom; each magnesium atom has 2 electrons to donate, so there are two chloride ions made for every magnesium ion; the ions come together to form a giant structure; called an ionic lattice; which is held together by the electrostatic forces; between ions; ionic substances conduct electricity; when molten; or in solution; because the ions are free to move; so there can be a flow of charged particles; which is a current; however, there is no conduction of electricity in solid magnesium chloride; as the ions are not free to move; the solid also has a high melting point; because the electrostatic forces between the ions are strong and the structure is giant; lots of energy to overcome them all; and melt the solid (6).

Physics practice exam

1 a) C (1)

b) The electrons in the paper are repelled away from the comb or a positive charge is induced on the pieces of paper (1); the positive charge left/induced charge is attracted to the comb (1).

c) The metal comb is a conductor (1) and the rubber gloves prevent the charge being conducted through your body to the Earth (1).

d) i) The charge moves in one direction (1).

ii) $I = Q/t = 360\,C/(60 \times 60)\,s$ or $360\,C/3600\,s$ (1) = 0.1 (1) A

2 a) Small nuclei (1) join together to make larger nuclei (1).

b) They give out (a lot of) energy (1).

c) The nuclei must be moving very fast (1) to overcome the (electrostatic) forces of repulsion between them (1). (Stating that the nuclei carry positive charges that repel will gain 1 mark.)

d) It is very difficult to maintain/sustain/control the high temperatures that are needed (1).

e) When the experiments have been repeated by other scientists (1) they have not given the same result (1). (stating that the work has not been 'validated' is worth 1 mark.)

3 a) 4 000 000 N (1)

b) 4 000 000 N − 3 200 000 N (1) = 800 000 N (1)

c) i) gradient of the line = change in velocity/time e.g. 20 m/s/8 s (1) = 2.5 (1) m/s² (the acceleration can also be calculated from the data given in the question, i.e. $a = F/m = 800\,000\,N/320\,000\,kg$ (1) = 2.5 (1) m/s²)

ii) distance = area under line = $\frac{1}{2} \times 5\,s \times 12.5\,m/s$ (1) = 31.25 (1) m

d) The air resistance increases reducing the acceleration (1); the mass of the rocket decreases (as the fuel is used up) so the acceleration increases (1). (The factor and the effect it has must be given for each mark.)

4 a) ammeter (A) in series anywhere in the circuit (1); voltmeter (V) in parallel with lamp (1)

b) $R = V/I = 12$ volts$/ 0.1$ A (1) = 120 (1) ohms

c) i) current increases with voltage/potential difference (1); but the gradient of increase in current decreases with increasing voltage/potential difference (1)

ii) potential difference/voltage is the energy transferred per unit/coulomb of charge (1)

iii) Energy is transferred when the moving electrons (1) collide with ions (1) in the metal wire.

iv) $P = I \times V = 0.5\,A \times 12\,V$ (1) = 6 (1) W

5 a) i) increases (1)

ii) increases (1)

iii) decreases (1)

b) i) $F = m(v - u)/t = 5\,kg \times (2 - 0\,m/s)/0.8\,s$ (1) = 12.5 (1) N

ii) C (1)

c) The white ball initially has momentum; the coloured ball initially has zero momentum; after the collision the momentum must be conserved; that is, the sum of the momentum of both balls must be the same as the white ball before collision.
Skilled player: all the momentum is transferred to the coloured ball; the coloured ball moves with the same velocity/speed in same direction as the white ball did; when the white ball hits the coloured ball its momentum changes and a force is applied to the coloured ball.
Unskilled player: the momentum of each ball is half of the white ball's; the white ball has a smaller change in momentum so there is a smaller force on the coloured ball; so the two balls travel at half the velocity that the white ball did; and in the same direction.
This is ignoring loss of energy due to friction with the table. More complicated situations can arise if the white ball hits the coloured ball off-centre (6).

6 a) Evidence was collected that ionising radiation harmed health/increased scientific knowledge about risks/harmful effects (1); so attitudes to safety precautions changed (1).

b) Ionising radiation damages tissues/kills cell (1), and can cause mutations/damage DNA (causing cancers) (1).

c) Any two from: the notebooks should be stored in a lead-lined container; they should be handled with tongs; scientists should wear protective clothing/gloves (2).

d) The nucleus of each isotope contains 88 protons; the nuclei of each isotope contain different numbers of neutrons; Ra-224 has 136, Ra-226 has 138, Ra-228 has 140 neutrons; samples of Ra-224 will have a much higher activity/decays per second than Ra-226; because the half-life of Ra-224 is much shorter; half of a sample of Ra-224 will have decayed in 4 days while it takes 1622 years for half of Ra-226 to decay (you would also get marks for making a similar comparison of any pair of the isotopes in the table); all of the isotopes are hazardous because they give off ionising radiation; they all give off gamma rays, which are most penetrating/need thick lead to absorb the rays; the beta radiation given off by Ra-228 is more penetrating that the alpha radiation given off by Ra-224 and Ra-226; beta radiation is stopped by thin sheets of aluminium; alpha radiation is stopped by a few cm of air or a sheet of paper (6).

Published by Pearson Education Limited, Edinburgh Gate, Harlow, Essex, CM20 2JE.

www.pearsonschoolsandfecolleges.co.uk

Copies of official specifications for all Edexcel qualifications may be found on the Edexcel website: www.edexcel.com

Text and original illustrations © Pearson Education Limited 2012
Edited by Gillian Lindsey and Florence Production Ltd
Typeset and illustrated by Tech-Set Ltd, Gateshead
Cover illustration by Miriam Sturdee

The rights of Peter Ellis, Damian Riddle and Ian Roberts to be identified as authors of this work have been asserted by them in accordance with the Copyright, Designs and Patents Act 1988.

First published 2012

16 15 14
10 9 8 7 6 5 4 3

British Library Cataloguing in Publication Data
A catalogue record for this book is available from the British Library

ISBN 978 1 446 90266 0

Printed in Slovakia by Neografia

Acknowledgements
Every effort has been made to contact copyright holders of material reproduced in this book. Any omissions will be rectified in subsequent printings if notice is given to the publishers.

In the writing of this book, no Edexcel examiners authored sections relevant to examination papers for which they have responsibility.